A2 Biology
UNITS 5 & 6

Edexcel

Unit 5: Genetics, Evolution and Biodiversity

Unit 6: Synoptic and Practical Assessment

Alan Clamp

To Aristos, Dave, Jon, Jules, Paul and Pete

Philip Allan Updates, an imprint of Hodder Education, part of Hachette Livre UK, Market Place, Deddington, Oxfordshire OX15 0SE

Orders

Bookpoint Ltd, 130 Milton Park, Abingdon, Oxfordshire, OX14 4SB
tel: 01235 827720
fax: 01235 400454
e-mail: uk.orders@bookpoint.co.uk
Lines are open 9.00 a.m.–5.00 p.m., Monday to Saturday, with a 24-hour message answering service. You can also order through the Philip Allan Updates website: www.philipallan.co.uk

© Philip Allan Updates 2002

ISBN 978-0-86003-472-8

This Guide has been written specifically to support students preparing for the Edexcel A2 Biology Unit 5 and Unit 6 examinations. The content has been neither approved nor endorsed by Edexcel and remains the sole responsibility of the author.

Printed by MPG Books, Bodmin

Hachette Livre UK's policy is to use papers that are natural, renewable and recyclable products and made from wood grown in sustainable forests. The logging and manufacturing processes are expected to conform to the environmental regulations of the country of origin.

Contents

Introduction

About this guide 4

The specification 4

Synoptic skills 5

Study skills and revision strategies 6

The unit tests 7

Practical assessment of coursework 10

■ ■ ■

Content Guidance

About this section 14

Photosynthesis 15

Control of growth in plants 20

Biodiversity 21

Genetics and evolution 25

■ ■ ■

Questions & Answers

About this section 38

Mock paper 1: Genetics, evolution and biodiversity (I) 39

Mock paper 2: Genetics, evolution and biodiversity (II) 43

Answers to mock paper 1: Candidate A 47

Answers to mock paper 1: Candidate B 52

Answers to mock paper 2: Candidate A 56

Answers to mock paper 2: Candidate B 61

Mock paper 3: Synoptic paper (I) 66

Mock paper 4: Synoptic paper (II) 69

Answers to mock paper 3: Candidate A 71

Answers to mock paper 3: Candidate B 74

Answers to mock paper 4: Candidate A 77

Answers to mock paper 4: Candidate B 79

Introduction

About this guide

This unit guide is the final book in a series of four, which together cover the whole Edexcel specification for AS and A2 biology. Its aim is to help you prepare for Unit Test 5 in A2 biology, which examines the core content of **Unit 5: Genetics, Evolution and Biodiversity**, and also for Unit Test 6, which includes synoptic assessment and coursework. There are three sections to this guide:

- **Introduction** — this provides advice on how to use the unit guide, an explanation of the skills required in A2 biology and suggestions for effective revision. It concludes with guidance on how to succeed in the unit tests.
- **Content Guidance** — this summarises the specification content of Unit 5 (there is no theoretical content in Unit 6).
- **Questions and Answers** — this section provides two Unit 5 mock test papers followed by two Unit 6 mock test papers for you to try, together with sample answers to these questions and examiner's comments on how they could have been improved.

An effective way to use this book is to read through this Introduction section at the beginning of your course to familiarise yourself with the skills required for A2 biology. Try to make a habit of using the study skills and revision advice suggested in this section. It may also help to refer back to this information at regular intervals during your course.

The Content Guidance section will be useful when you are revising a topic because it highlights the main points of each subsection of the Unit 5 specification. You may want to 'tick-off' topics as you learn them to make sure that you have revised everything thoroughly.

Finally, the mock tests in the Question and Answer section will provide some very useful practice when preparing for the unit tests.

The specification

In order to make a good start to Unit 5 and Unit 6, it is important to have a close look at the specification. Your teacher should have one, or you can obtain your own copy from the awarding body (Edexcel). In addition to describing the content of the units, the specification provides information about the unit tests. It is important for you to understand the key terms used in the specification, as defined below.

- **Recall** — identify and revise biological knowledge gained from previous studies of biology.

- **Know** — be able to state facts, or describe structures and processes, from material within the unit.
- **Understand** — explain the underlying principles and apply this knowledge to new situations.
- **Appreciate** — be aware of the importance of biological information, without having a detailed knowledge of the underlying principles.
- **Discuss** — provide a balanced, reasoned and objective review of a particular topic.
- **Describe** — provide an accurate account of the main points (an explanation is not necessary).
- **Explain** — give reasons, with reference to biological theories.

The specification also provides information about the skills required in A2 biology. For example, in Unit 5 approximately 17% of the marks are available for showing *knowledge and understanding* of biological information, and a further 17% of the marks are available for *applying* this knowledge and understanding to explain experimental data or solve problems in unfamiliar situations. The remaining 66% of the marks are for demonstrating *synoptic skills*, as described below. In the written paper for Unit 6, *all* the marks are allocated to synoptic skills.

Finally, in addition to looking at the specification, it would also be useful for you to read the examiners' reports and published mark schemes from previous unit tests (these are available from Edexcel). These documents will show you the depth of knowledge that examiners are looking for in answers, as well as pointing out common mistakes and providing advice on how to achieve good grades in the tests.

Synoptic skills

The Edexcel specification states that students should be able to:
- bring together principles and concepts from different areas of biology and apply them in a particular context
- use biological skills in those contexts that bring together different areas of the subject
- express ideas clearly and logically, using appropriate specialist vocabulary

Synoptic questions, therefore, require you to make connections between the facts or principles in different units. For example, an essay on the roles of carbohydrates in living organisms may require you to mention their structural roles (e.g. deoxyribose in DNA), as well as their transport roles (e.g. sucrose in the phloem of flowering plants), with this information coming from different units.

One-fifth (20%) of your marks in A-level biology are allocated to synoptic skills, which is more than any single 'content-based' unit. It is vital, therefore, that you practise these skills and familiarise yourself with the style of synoptic questions, as shown in the Question and Answer section in this guide.

Study skills and revision strategies

Students need to develop good study skills if they are to be successful. This section of the Introduction provides advice and guidance on how to study A2 biology and suggests some strategies for effective revision.

Organising your notes

Biology students usually accumulate a large quantity of notes and it is useful to keep this information in an organised manner. The presentation of notes is important; good notes should always be clear and concise. You could try organising your notes under headings and subheadings, with key points highlighted using capitals, italics or colour. Numbered lists are useful, as are tables and diagrams. It is a good idea to file your notes in specification order, using a consistent series of informative headings, as illustrated below.

> ### UNIT 5 (Genetics, Evolution and Biodiversity)
> **Photosynthesis**
> *The light-dependent reaction*
> *The light-dependent reaction is the process in which light energy is absorbed by chlorophyll and used to produce ATP and reduced NADP...*

After each lesson, it is a good idea to check your notes using your textbook(s) and fill in any gaps in the information. Make sure you go back and ask the teacher if you are unsure about anything, especially if you find conflicting information in your class notes and textbook.

Organising your time

It is a good idea to make a revision timetable to ensure you use your time effectively. This should allow enough time to cover all the material, but also be realistic. For example, it is useful to leave some time at the end of the timetable, just before the unit test, to catch up on time lost, possibly through illness. You may not be able to work for very long at a single session — probably no more than 1 hour — without a short break of 10–15 minutes. It is also useful to use spare moments, such as when waiting for a bus or train, to do short snippets of revision. These 'odd minutes' can add up to many hours.

Improving your memory

There are several things you can do to improve the effectiveness of your memory for biological information. Organising the material will help, especially if you use topic headings, numbered lists and diagrams. Repeatedly reviewing your notes will also be useful, as will discussing topics with teachers and other students. Finally, using mnemonics (memory aids), such as **A**rteries carry blood **A**way from the heart, can make a big difference.

Revision strategies

To revise a topic effectively you should work carefully through your notes, using a copy of the specification to make sure you have not missed anything out. Summarise your notes to the bare essentials, using the tips given on note-making above. Finally, use the content guidance and mock examinations in this book, discussing any difficulties with your teachers or other students.

In many ways, a student should prepare for a unit test like an athlete prepares for a major event, such as the Olympic Games. The athlete will train every day for weeks or months before the event, practising the required skills in order to achieve the best performance on the day. So it is with test preparation: everything you do should contribute to your chances of success in the unit test.

The following points summarise some of the strategies that you may wish to use to make sure that your revision is as effective as possible.

- Use a revision timetable.
- Ideally, revise in a quiet room, sitting at a desk or table, with no distractions.
- Test yourself regularly to assess the effectiveness of your revision.
- Practise previous test questions to highlight gaps in your knowledge and understanding and to improve your technique.
- Active revision is much better than simply reading over material. Discuss topics, summarise notes and use the mock tests included in this book to increase the effectiveness of your revision.

The unit tests

Unit Test 5 consists of about eight compulsory questions allocated from 4 to 12 marks each, presented in a question–answer booklet. There are 70 marks available in this test which lasts for 1 hour 30 minutes (giving you approximately 1.3 minutes per mark). There are two sections to the paper — Unit 5 and the synoptic section. The shorter questions in Unit 5 are designed mainly to test knowledge and understanding of the unit content. The longer questions in this section also test skills of interpretation of data that are related to the content of the unit. The synoptic section tests your ability to make connections between at least two units of the specification, and to use the skills and ideas you have developed throughout the course in new contexts. There will be a free-prose question in this section (see p. 8).

Unit Test 6 (the synoptic paper) consists of three questions presented in a question–answer booklet. There are 38 marks available in this test which lasts for 1 hour 10 minutes (giving you approximately 1.8 minutes per mark). There are two compulsory structured questions plus one essay, chosen from two titles.

There are a number of terms commonly used in unit tests. It is important that you understand the meaning of each of these terms and that you answer the question appropriately.

- **Calculate** — carry out a calculation, showing your working and providing the appropriate units.
- **Compare** — point out similarities *and* differences.
- **Define** — give a statement outlining what is meant by a particular term.
- **Describe** — provide an accurate account of the main points. An explanation is *not* necessary.
- **Discuss** — describe and evaluate, putting forward the various opinions on a topic.
- **Distinguish between** — point out differences only.
- **Explain** — give reasons, with reference to biological facts. A description is *not* required.
- **Outline** — give a brief account.
- **Significance** — the relevance of an idea or observation.
- **State** — give a concise, factual answer (also applies to **give** or **name**).
- **Suggest** — use biological knowledge to put forward an appropriate answer in an unfamiliar situation.
- **What/Why/Where** — these indicate direct questions requiring concise answers.

Whatever the question style, you must read the question *very carefully*, underline key words or phrases, think about your response and allocate time according to the number of marks available. Further advice and guidance on answering test questions is provided in the Question and Answer section at the end of this book.

Structured questions

These are short-answer questions that may require a single-word answer, a short sentence, or a response amounting to several sentences. Answers should be clear, concise and to the point. The marks allocated and the space provided for the answer usually give an indication of the amount of detail required. Typical question styles include:
- naming parts on diagrams
- filling in gaps in a prose passage
- completing tables and tick-boxes
- plotting graphs
- performing calculations
- interpreting experimental data

Free-prose questions

These questions enable you to demonstrate the depth and breadth of your biological knowledge, as well as your ability to communicate scientific ideas in a concise and clear manner. The following points should help you to perform well when answering free-prose questions:

- make your points clearly and concisely, illustrating your answer with examples where appropriate
- try to avoid repetition and keep the answer relevant (refer back to the question)
- your points should cover the *full range* of the topics addressed in the question
- use diagrams only if appropriate and where they make a useful contribution to the quality of your answer
- the time you spend on the question should be proportional to the marks available

Essays (Unit 6)

Essay questions test your ability to describe and explain biological systems and processes and also your understanding of biological principles and concepts. In the essay, you may be required to sustain an argument, to present evidence for and against a statement and to show that you are aware of the implications and applications of modern biology. To score high marks in an essay, you need to consider the points made about free-prose questions above and also make sure that you develop a coherent argument and demonstrate high-quality written communication skills.

The following tips may be useful when tackling synoptic essay questions.

- *Read* the question(s) carefully. It is surprising how many candidates misread questions, for example mixing up the terms 'mitosis' and 'meiosis'.
- *Choose* the essay carefully. You have a choice of two titles, so you should think about which will earn you most marks. It is worth spending a short period of time jotting down what you know about a topic in order to make the right choice. There is nothing worse that writing half an essay on one topic and then abandoning it to start on the essay you should have picked in the first place!
- *Before* you start writing the essay, you need to jot down all of your ideas. Then organise these ideas into a logical sequence, ignoring issues that you decide are not relevant. Group ideas together, to form the subsections or paragraphs for your essay. This is your essay plan.
- *Review* your plan to make sure that it is *balanced*, i.e. that it contains a range of ideas from several parts of the specification (AS *and* A2). For example, if the essay is about 'nitrogenous excretion in living organisms', make sure that you include a wide range of organisms and not just mammals (or even worse, just humans). Similarly, if the question specifies animals *and* plants, make sure that you give approximately equal weighting to both — don't write an essay on animals and then add on a brief paragraph about plants at the end.
- *Structure* your essay. It should start with an introductory paragraph that 'sets the scene' and introduces the topic in general terms. This should be followed by the main part of the essay, where you present your detailed discussion or argument. The essay should finish with a concluding paragraph summarising the overall content. While you are writing, it is a good idea to refer back to your plan and tick-off points that you have covered. This ensures that you do not repeat yourself or miss anything out. It also helps you to avoid going 'off the point' and writing an essay about an entirely different topic!

Diagrams can be useful in an essay, but if you are going to use diagrams it is important to remember the following points:

- diagrams should be large, clearly drawn and accurately labelled or annotated
- do *not* repeat information in a diagram that is already covered by what you have written — diagrams should complement the writing and add new information
- be careful of time if including several diagrams — they often take longer than a written paragraph that would earn just as many marks
- if you are not sure whether to include a diagram in your essay, the best option is probably to leave it out

Don't forget that you will also be judged on your *communication skills*. You should write your answer in sentences and paragraphs (*not* bullet points). Try to make sure that your writing is well-organised, legible, with good grammar and spelling.

The day of the unit test

On the day of the test, make sure that you have:

- two or more blue/black pens, and two or more pencils
- your calculator plus spare batteries
- a watch to check the time
- a ruler and an eraser

Read each question very carefully so that your answers are appropriate. Make sure that you write legibly (you will not be given marks if the examiner cannot read what you have written) and try to spell scientific terms accurately. If you need more room for your answer, look for space at the bottom of the page, the end of the question or after the last question, or use supplementary sheets. If you use these spaces, or sheets, alert the examiner by adding 'continued below', or 'continued on page X'.

Time is often a problem. Make sure that you know how long you have got for the whole test and how many questions you have to do in this time. You could use the number of minutes per mark to work out approximately how long you have for each question (e.g. 10 minutes for an 8-mark question in Unit Test 5).

Do not write out the question, but try to make a number of valid points that correspond to the number of marks available. If you get stuck, make a note of the question number and move on. Later, if you have time, go back and try that difficult question again.

Finally, it is a good idea to leave a few minutes at the end to check through your answers, correcting any mistakes or filling in any gaps.

Practical assessment of coursework

The individual study in Unit 6 involves the assessment of practical skills through coursework. The aim of the investigation is to give you the opportunity to plan and carry out a scientific experiment on your own. You then need to write a detailed account of your investigation, which is marked partly by your teacher (planning and implementing) and partly by Edexcel (all other skills).

In the individual study, marks are awarded for the following skills:
- planning (4)
- implementing (4)
- introduction (4)
- method (3)
- analysis (6)
- discussion (8)
- style (3)

It is very useful to have a copy of the mark scheme when you are planning, carrying out and writing up your study. You are more likely to get a good grade if you know how the marks are awarded. Further information about the practical assessment of coursework can be found in the specification.

Content
Guidance

Unit 5: Genetics, Evolution and Biodiversity includes the sub-topics of:

(1) Photosynthesis

(2) Control of growth in plants

(3) Biodiversity

(4) Genetics and evolution

You may be familiar with some of the information in this unit, but it is important that you know and understand this information exactly as described in the specification. This summary of the specification content will highlight the key points and should prove very useful when learning and revising biology.

Note that there is no content guidance for Unit 6. This unit assesses your synoptic and practical skills.

Photosynthesis

Photosynthesis is the process by which organic compounds are synthesised from carbon dioxide and water using light energy. This process takes place in the chloroplasts of green plants. The diagram below shows the structure of a chloroplast.

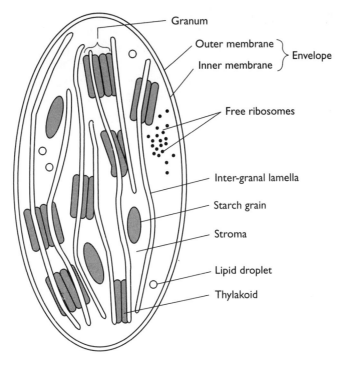

The chemical reactions that take place during photosynthesis are summarised in the following flowchart.

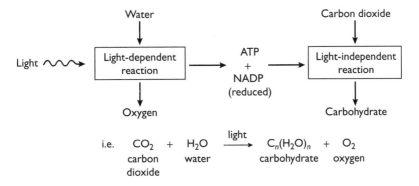

Photosynthesis occurs in two stages: the **light-dependent reaction** and the **light-independent reaction**. It is important to remember that the light-dependent reaction can only take place in the light. The light-independent reaction requires substances produced in the light before it can proceed. Therefore, the light-independent reaction also takes place in the light.

Light-dependent reaction

This is the process by which light energy is absorbed by chlorophyll and used to produce ATP and reduced NADP during photosynthesis. The light-dependent reaction takes place on the grana of chloroplasts and consists of two processes:

- **Cyclic photophosphorylation** — light energy causes the emission of a high-energy electron from chlorophyll. This electron is passed back to the chlorophyll molecule via an electron transport chain, generating ATP.
- **Non-cyclic photophosphorylation** — light energy causes the emission of a high-energy electron from chlorophyll. This electron is passed along an electron transport chain (generating ATP) and is used to reduce NADP. Chlorophyll has its electron replaced by the photolysis (splitting) of water, resulting in the production of oxygen.

The light-dependent reaction is summarised in the diagram below.

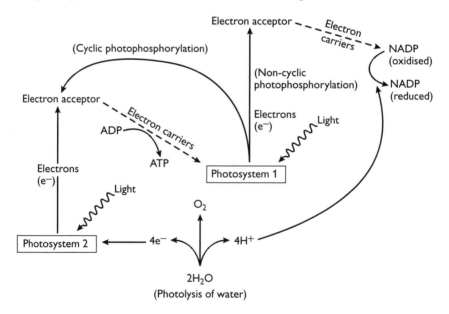

Light-independent reaction

This is the process by which carbon dioxide is fixed and reduced to carbohydrate during photosynthesis. Carbon dioxide is fixed by ribulose bisphosphate (RuBP), generating two molecules of glycerate 3-phosphate (phosphoglyceric acid, PGA). ATP and reduced NADP (from the light-dependent reaction) then convert glycerate 3-phosphate to glyceraldehyde 3-phosphate (triose phosphate). This can be used to regenerate RuBP (to fix more carbon dioxide), or it can be built up into carbohydrates, lipids, proteins and nucleic acids. The light-independent reaction takes place in the stroma of chloroplasts.

The light-independent reaction is summarised in the diagram below.

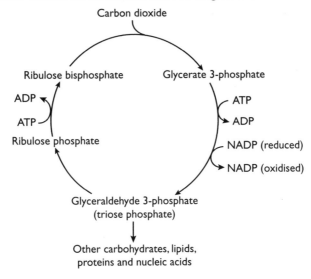

Leaf structure

In addition to the biochemistry of photosynthesis, it is important that you can describe the external and internal structure of a typical dicotyledonous leaf and of a palisade cell, as shown below.

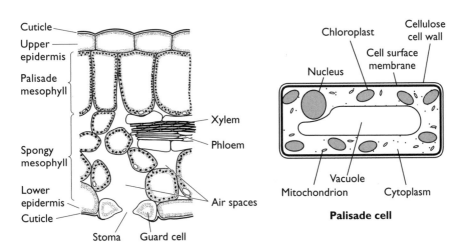

Palisade cell

You also need to understand the nature of chloroplast pigments, particularly chlorophyll. Chlorophyll is actually a group of pigments, each consisting of a complex organic molecule containing magnesium. The most common forms are chlorophyll a (a blue-green pigment) and chlorophyll b (a yellow-green pigment). Chlorophyll molecules are responsible for the capture of light energy and therefore play a key role in the light-dependent stage of photosynthesis.

An **absorption spectrum** is a graph showing the relative amounts of light of different wavelengths that are absorbed by a pigment. The diagram below shows the absorption spectrum for chlorophyll a.

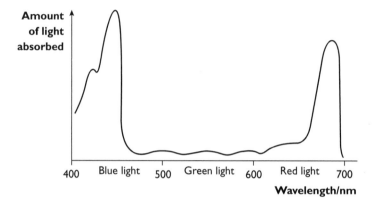

Chlorophyll absorbs light strongly at the blue and red ends of the spectrum, and reflects green light. This is why most leaves appear green.

An **action spectrum** is a graph showing the relative amounts of light of different wavelengths that are used in a particular process, such as photosynthesis. The action spectrum for photosynthesis is shown in the diagram below. Note that it is similar to the absorption spectrum for chlorophyll a. This suggests that most of the light absorbed by chlorophyll is used in photosynthesis.

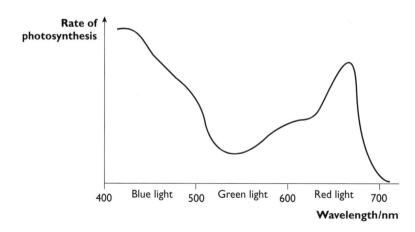

Environmental factors affecting photosynthesis

The rate of photosynthesis is determined by light intensity, carbon dioxide concentration and temperature, according to the concept of **limiting factors**. Blackman's law of limiting factors states that 'when a process is controlled by a number of factors, the factor in least supply will limit the rate of the process'. For example, the graph below shows how light intensity affects the rate of photosynthesis.

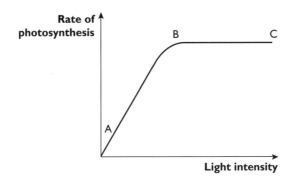

At low light intensity, between the points **A** and **B** on the graph, the rate of photosynthesis is limited by the amount of light available. An increase in light intensity will produce an increase on the rate of photosynthesis. Between points **B** and **C**, however, increasing the light intensity has no effect on the rate of photosynthesis, so another factor must be limiting. In this case, it is probably temperature or the concentration of carbon dioxide which is the limiting factor. Increasing either (or both) of these factors may cause an increase in the rate of photosynthesis. (Note that the point on the graph where the rate of photosynthesis is the same as the rate of respiration is known as the **compensation point**.)

Mineral nutrition

In addition to carbon dioxide and water, flowering plants need a number of essential elements to remain healthy. The roots take up these elements in the form of mineral (inorganic) ions from the soil water.

- **Nitrogen** is taken up as nitrate ions for the synthesis of amino acids, proteins and nucleic acids.
- **Phosphorus** is taken up as phosphate ions for the synthesis of nucleic acids, phospholipids and ATP.
- **Magnesium** is taken up as magnesium ions for the synthesis of chlorophyll and as an activator for many enzymes.

The ions are taken up by diffusion and/or active transport and travel across the root by either the **symplast** pathway (through the cytoplasm and plasmodesmata) or the **apoplast** pathway (through the cell walls).

Practical work

You are expected to have carried out practical work to include:
- the chromatography of chloroplast pigments
- experiments to investigate the effects of light intensity and carbon dioxide concentration on the rate of photosynthesis
- the investigation of plant growth by mineral culture solutions

Control of growth in plants

Phytochrome is a pigment found in plants that is important in regulating growth. The pigment exists in two forms. P_R has a maximum light absorption peak in red light of wavelength 660 nm, whereas P_{FR} absorbs maximally in far red light at 730 nm. The two forms are interconvertible, as shown in the diagram below.

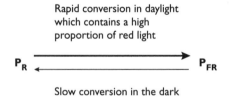

Rapid conversion in daylight which contains a high proportion of red light

P_R ⟶ P_{FR}

Slow conversion in the dark

P_{FR} is thought to be metabolically active, influencing a number of light-related processes, including germination and flowering.

Plant growth substances are organic compounds that play an important role in the coordination of plant growth and development. There are five key growth substances: abscisic acid, auxins, cytokinins, ethene and gibberellins.
- **Abscisic acid (ABA)** — a plant growth substance that acts mainly as a growth inhibitor. ABA stimulates the closing of stomata and may play a part in leaf fall in some deciduous trees. It also inhibits germination in seeds.
- **Auxins** — a group of plant growth substances that act mainly as growth stimulators. Auxins stimulate cell division, cell elongation, fruit development and (at low concentrations) root growth. They also inhibit lateral bud development, leaf and fruit abscission and (at high concentrations) root growth. Many auxins have commercial applications, for example as herbicides.
- **Cytokinin** — a plant growth substance which stimulates cell division. Cytokinins also promote the growth of lateral buds and leaves in stems, and delay senescence (ageing) in leaves.

- **Ethene** — a gaseous hydrocarbon (C_2H_4) which acts as a plant growth substance. Ethene stimulates the ripening of fruit and, in some species, breaks the dormancy of buds and seeds.
- **Gibberellin** — a plant growth substance that acts mainly as a growth stimulator. Gibberellin stimulates germination, cell elongation in the stem and the breaking of dormancy in buds.

These plant growth substances may act **synergistically** (their combined action produces a greater effect than would be expected from adding the individual effects of each substance) or **antagonistically** (their combined action produces a smaller effect than would be expected from adding the individual effects of each substance).

Practical work

You are expected to have carried out practical work on the effects of plant growth substances, for example rooting powder and weed killers, on plant growth.

Biodiversity

Classification

Classification is the system by which living organisms are organised into groups. The most useful classification system is based on the evolutionary relationships between organisms and has a hierarchical structure. All organisms belong to one of five **kingdoms** — Animalia, Fungi, Plantae, Prokaryotae and Protoctista.

Animalia — the kingdom containing animals. All animals share the following features:
- they are multicellular organisms
- their cells do not possess cell walls
- they show heterotrophic nutrition

Examples include starfish (members of the phylum Echinodermata) and lizards (members of the phylum Chordata).

Fungi — the kingdom containing mushrooms, toadstools, moulds and yeasts. All fungi share the following features:
- they are heterotrophic
- they reproduce by means of spores
- they are usually made up of thread-like structures known as hyphae
- most have cell walls made of chitin

Plantae — the kingdom containing plants. All plants share the following features:
- they are multicellular organisms
- their cells possess cell walls composed mainly of cellulose

- they show autotrophic nutrition
- they have a lifecycle that shows alternation of generations

Examples include mosses (members of the phylum Bryophyta), ferns (members of the phylum Filicinophyta) and flowering plants (members of the phylum Angiospermophyta).

Protoctista — the kingdom containing eukaryotic organisms that cannot be classified as members of the Fungi, Animalia or Plantae kingdoms. Examples include red algae, slime moulds and amoeba.

Prokaryotae — the kingdom that includes bacteria. Prokaryotic cells have a different structure to all other (eukaryotic) cells. The main differences are summarised in the table below.

Feature	Prokaryotic cells	Eukaryotic cells
Size	Cells smaller, usually less than 5 μm in diameter	Cells larger, often as much as 50 μm in diameter
Nucleus and DNA	Cells do not have a nucleus. The DNA, which is not associated with proteins, is present as a circular strand in the cytoplasm of the cell	Cells have a nucleus. The DNA, which is in long strands, is associated with proteins forming chromosomes
Organelles	Few organelles present and none of them are surrounded by a membrane	Many membrane-surrounded organelles, such as mitochondria, present
Ribosomes	Only have small ribosomes which are free in the cytoplasm	Have small ribosomes and larger ones which are associated with membranes forming rough endoplasmic reticulum

Each kingdom can be subdivided into a number of phyla. Each phylum can also be divided into classes, and so on. The smallest group is an individual species. The table below shows how humans are classified.

Kingdom	Animalia
Phylum	Chordata
Class	Mammalia
Order	Primates
Family	Hominidae
Genus	*Homo*
Species	*sapiens*

Remember that the correct order of the various classification groups is: kingdom, phylum, class, order, family, genus, species. Try to devise a suitable memory-aid to help you learn this sequence, such as Keep Plucking Chickens Or Fear Getting Sacked.

Distribution of plants and animals

The distribution of plants and animals within a habitat (e.g. a pond or a woodland) is determined by a combination of abiotic and biotic factors.

- Abiotic factor — any of the non-living factors that make up the environment of living organisms. Examples include rainfall, soil pH, temperature and light intensity.
- Biotic factor — any environmental factor that is associated with living organisms. Examples include predation, competition and food availability.

Succession

The progressive change that occurs in a community of organisms over a period of time is known as **succession**. It starts with the initial colonisation of an area and usually progresses through several distinct stages before reaching a stable climax community. A succession that is prevented from reaching its natural climax (usually as a result of human activity) is called a deflected succession.

Populations

A **population** is a group of individuals of the same species occupying a certain area. (Members of a population are capable of interbreeding and therefore share the same gene pool.) A **community** is all the living organisms present in a habitat. For example, a climax community represents the different species of organisms present at the end of a succession, such as oak woodland in many parts of the UK.

Population **size** refers to the total number of individuals present in a given area, whereas population **density** is a measure of the number of individual organisms per unit area. Both are affected by a number of **density-dependent** and **density-independent** factors.

- **Density-dependent factor** — any factor limiting the size of a population whose effect is proportional to the density of the population. These factors tend to be **biotic**, for example food supply (for both predators and prey) and infectious diseases.
- **Density-independent factor** — any factor limiting the size of a population whose effect is independent of the density of the population. These factors tend to be **abiotic**, for example temperature and water availability.

The maximum population size that can be sustained by a particular habitat is known as the **carrying capacity** of that area. Populations are prevented from growing beyond the carrying capacity by a combination of density-dependent and density-independent factors, which constitute **environmental resistance**. An important component of this environmental resistance is competition between individuals, which may be either **interspecific** or **intraspecific**.

- **Interspecific competition** — competition for resources that occurs between members of different species. This occurs mainly among organisms on the same trophic level, competing for the same food supply.
- **Intraspecific competition** — competition for resources that occurs between members of the same species. Members of the same species can compete for food, mates or nesting sites.

Control of insect populations

Populations of insect pests can be controlled using both chemical and biological methods.

Chemical control — the use of pesticides (insecticides), such as DDT. The disadvantages of pesticides are:

- they may be toxic to non-target organisms
- they may be non-biodegradeable, so that they persist in the environment
- they may bioaccumulate in living organisms (become concentrated in the bodies of animals found at the top of food chains)
- their frequent use can result in the pest population becoming resistant to their effects

Biological control — the use of a parasite or a predator to control the number of pest organisms in a particular area. For example, aphids (insect pests of plants) are controlled by the use of ladybird beetles. Biological control also includes breeding pest-resistant crops. It has a number of advantages over chemical control:

- it is very specific
- it needs fewer applications and is therefore often cheaper than chemical control
- pests do not usually become resistant to biological control
- it does not pollute the environment

However, there are also disadvantages to biological control:

- it is relatively slow compared with chemical control
- pests are never completely eliminated, so there is always some damage to crops
- the control organism may become a pest in its own right

Conservation

Conservation is the process of maintaining an ecosystem in order to retain maximum species diversity. This involves careful use of the earth's natural resources in order to avoid the gradual destruction of the environment by human activities. It also involves preservation of natural habitats and an awareness of the dangers of pollution.

You are expected to be able to describe and explain:
- the management of grassland and woodland habitats to maintain or increase biodiversity, as illustrated by mowing, grazing, scrub clearance, use of fire and coppicing
- how intensive food production can affect wildlife
- how farming practice can enhance biodiversity
- the significance of the EU Habitats Directive and of Natura 2000

Note that it would be useful to review the basic principles of ecology learned in Unit 3 in order to understand fully this section of the specification.

Practical work

You are also expected to have carried out practical work to include:
- the study of the distribution of plants and animals in at least one habitat and investigations of the influence of abiotic factors on them
- the estimation of population size using the Lincoln index

Genetics and evolution

In order to understand the topics covered in this section, it is important to know the terminology of genetics.

Genes and alleles

A **gene** is a section of DNA that codes for the production of a particular polypeptide or protein. A gene can also be defined as a unit of heredity that is found at a specific position on a chromosome. Different forms of a particular gene are known as **alleles**. Note that many students confuse the terms gene and allele. Remember that a gene controls a character, such as eye colour, and that alleles control different forms of this character, such as blue, green or brown eyes.

The **genotype** is the genetic composition of an organism. The genotype of an organism is the sum total of all the alleles present. However, we normally only consider one or two genes. Genotypes are usually represented by symbols. For example, the inheritance of height in garden peas is controlled by two alleles: T (the tall allele) and t (the short allele). The possible genotypes of a pea plant are therefore TT, Tt or tt, as there must be two alleles present for each characteristic. TT and tt are known as

homozygous genotypes (the alleles are the *same*) and Tt is known as the **heterozygous** genotype (the alleles are *different*).

The **phenotype** is the physical expression of the genotype of an organism. For example, a pea plant contains alleles that influence its height. In this case, the phenotype (appearance) of the pea plant could be either tall or short. It is important to note that the environment can have significant effects on the phenotype of an organism. For example, a pea plant may have the required genetic composition to be tall, but without appropriate amounts of light and water it will not reach its maximum height.

Dominant describes any allele that is always expressed in the phenotype of an organism. For example, in peas the allele for a tall plant (T) is dominant over that for a short plant (t). Therefore, pea plants with the genotype TT or Tt will be tall.

Recessive describes any allele that is only expressed in the phenotype of an organism if the dominant allele is not present. For example, in peas the allele for a short plant (t) is recessive to that for a tall plant (T). Therefore, only pea plants with the genotype tt will be short.

Codominant describes any two alleles that are both expressed in the phenotype of a heterozygous organism. For example, the gene C for coat colour in cattle has two co-dominant alleles, C^R (red hairs) and C^W (white hairs). A heterozygous individual ($C^R C^W$) will have a mixture of red and white hairs, giving an overall colour known as roan.

Multiple alleles is a condition in which a single gene has three or more alleles controlling a particular characteristic. For example, a single gene with three alleles (I^A, I^B and I^O) controls ABO blood groups in humans. Each person can only possess two of these alleles. I^A and I^B are codominant and are both dominant to I^O. Therefore, the possible genotypes and phenotypes (blood groups) are as follows:
- $I^A I^A$ or $I^A I^O$ = blood group A
- $I^B I^B$ or $I^B I^O$ = blood group B
- $I^A I^B$ = blood group AB
- $I^O I^O$ = blood group O

Note that multiple alleles are sometimes confused with **polygenes** (see page 29). In multiple allele systems, there is only *one* gene, but there are several (three or more) different alleles, i.e. different forms of the gene. The environment usually has little effect on the phenotype. Polygenic inheritance involves several different genes, which interact with the environment to produce the phenotype.

Monohybrid inheritance is the inheritance of a single characteristic. The different forms of the characteristic are controlled by different alleles of the same gene. For example, a monohybrid cross between two pure-breeding pea plants, one with yellow seeds and one with green seeds, would be expected to produce an F_1 (first) generation with only yellow seeds. This is because yellow coloration is dominant, and green coloration is recessive. If these F_1 plants are interbred, the F_2 (second) generation will have a mixture of yellow and green seeds in a ratio of 3:1. This monohybrid cross is summarised in the diagram below.

Let the alleles be represented by the following letters:
B = yellow; b = green

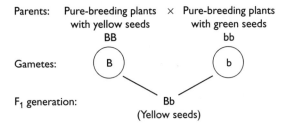

Parents: Pure-breeding plants × Pure-breeding plants
            with yellow seeds   with green seeds
                  BB   bb

Gametes: B   b

F_1 generation: Bb
                        (Yellow seeds)

Interbreeding the F_1 generation:

		Male gametes	
		B	b
Female gametes	B	BB yellow	Bb yellow
	b	Bb yellow	bb green

3 yellow seeds : 1 green seed

Sex determination is the mechanism by which sex is determined in a species. Female mammals have two X chromosomes and are known as the homogametic sex. This is because all eggs (gametes) produced by a female contain an X chromosome. Male mammals, on the other hand, have one X and one Y chromosome and are known as the heterogametic sex because sperm contain either an X chromosome or a Y chromosome. Since there is an equal chance that the sperm that fuses with an egg during fertilisation will have an X or a Y chromosome, it would be expected that approximately equal numbers of males and females will be produced.

Dihybrid inheritance is the inheritance of two different characteristics, controlled by genes at different loci (positions on a chromosome). If the genes are on the same chromosome they will show linkage (see page 29). If, however, the genes are on different chromosomes, they will show independent assortment. For example: a dihybrid cross between two pure-breeding pea plants, one with smooth yellow seeds and one with wrinkled green seeds, would be expected to produce an F_1 (first) generation with only smooth yellow seeds. This is because smooth texture and yellow coloration are dominant, and wrinkled texture and green coloration are recessive. If these F_1 plants are interbred (and assuming the genes for seed texture and colour are on different chromosomes), the F_2 (second) generation will have a mixture of seeds — smooth yellow, smooth green, wrinkled yellow and wrinkled green — in a ratio of 9:3:3:1. This dihybrid cross is summarised in the diagram below.

Let the alleles be represented by the following letters:
A = smooth; B = yellow; a = wrinkled; b = green

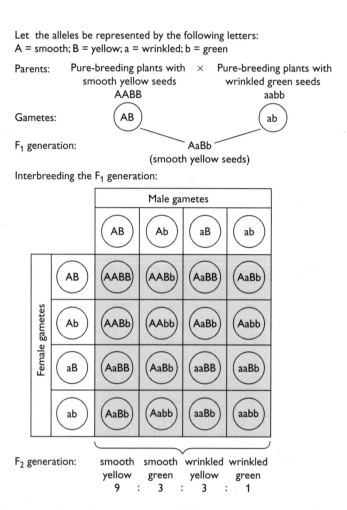

Parents: Pure-breeding plants with   ×   Pure-breeding plants with
             smooth yellow seeds   wrinkled green seeds
             AABB   aabb

Gametes: AB   ab

F₁ generation: AaBb
                       (smooth yellow seeds)

Interbreeding the F₁ generation:

F₂ generation: smooth   smooth   wrinkled   wrinkled
                   yellow   green   yellow   green
                     9   :   3   :   3   :   1

Epistasis is a type of gene interaction, in which one gene controls the expression of another gene. For example, two genes control fur colour in guinea pigs. If an animal has a dominant allele A, it will have coloured fur, otherwise it will be albino (white). If it also has dominant allele B, it will have black fur, otherwise its fur will be brown. In other words: all animals without A will be white; those with A and not B will be brown; and those with A and B will be black. The possible genotypes and phenotypes of these guinea pigs are summarised in the table below.

Genotypes	Phenotype (fur colour)
AABB, AaBB, AABb, AaBb	Black
AAbb, Aabb	Brown
aaBB, aaBb, aabb	White

Linkage is a term used to describe the relationship between different genes located on the same chromosome. Genes on a particular chromosome will normally be inherited together, as a linkage group, unless they are separated during crossing-over. Genes located on the sex chromosomes will normally be inherited along with sex (male or female) and are said to be sex-linked. Note that if during breeding experiments there is little independent assortment of two or more characteristics, it is likely that the genes controlling these characteristics are linked.

Note that it is a good idea to practise writing out genetic crosses, as in the examples described above. Try to remember the following points.

- Set your work out clearly, labelling the parents, gametes and new generations.
- Do not confuse the terms genotype and phenotype, or gene and allele.
- Do not represent alleles with letters that look similar in capitals and lower case, such as S and s, or K and k.
- Remember that gametes are haploid, so they only have one of each pair of alleles.
- Be aware that a ratio of 9:3:3:1 (or any other genetic ratio) is only what we would *expect* to find. The actual numbers of the different organisms will often be slightly different. If you do not find the ratio you expect, it could be a case of linkage.

Variation

Variation between members of the same species can be **continuous** or **discontinuous**. Continuous variation is variation of a characteristic within a population such that a complete range of forms can be seen. Height in humans is a good example of continuous variation. Within limits, any height is possible, as shown in the graph below.

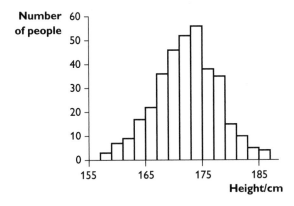

Continuous variation usually occurs when characters are controlled by a number of different genes (**polygenes**) and where the environment plays a significant role.

Discontinuous variation is a type of variation in which there are clearly defined differences within a population. In general, one or two genes determine discontinuous characteristics and the environment has little or no effect on the final pattern of variation. For example, ABO blood groups in humans are controlled by a single gene, and an individual will either be group A, B, AB or O, with no intermediate forms.

Sources of new inherited variation

In order to understand how genes can be recombined to produce new inherited variation, it is important to know the details of meiosis. Meiosis is a type of cell division used in the production of gametes. It involves two successive divisions of a diploid cell (in which the nucleus contains two complete sets of chromosomes), resulting in the production of haploid gametes (in which the nucleus contains only one complete set of chromosomes). This is summarised in the table below.

Stage	First division	Second division
Prophase	Homologous chromosomes form pairs and may exchange genetic material during crossing-over	Individual chromosomes can be seen to consist of a pair of chromatids
Metaphase	Homologous pairs line up at random on the equator of the cell, attached to spindle fibres by their centromeres	Individual chromosomes line up at random on the equator of the cell, attached to spindle fibres by their centromeres
Anaphase	Homologous chromosomes separate and move to opposite ends of the dividing cell	Chromatids separate and move to opposite ends of the dividing cell
Telophase	The first division is completed	The second division is completed and four gametes are produced from the original parent cell

Genetic variation arises as a result of crossing-over in prophase I, together with the random assortment of homologous chromosomes in metaphase I and random fertilisation during sexual reproduction.

Mutation is another source of new inherited variation and refers to any change in the amount or arrangement of DNA in a cell. There are two types of mutation:

- **Point (gene) mutations** — changes in the sequence of bases in DNA due to the deletion, insertion or substitution of a base. An example of a condition caused by a point mutation is sickle-cell anaemia.
- **Chromosome mutations** — changes in the structure or number of chromosomes. Changes in structure can be due to the deletion or translocation of part of a chromosome. Changes in number can be due to **polysomy** or **polyploidy**.

Polysomy is a condition in which an organism usually has one more or one fewer chromosome than normal. In cases of polysomy, the number of that particular chromosome is not diploid. In other words, there may be one or three copies of the chromosome rather than the expected two copies. Polysomy is usually caused by non-disjunction (the failure of a pair of homologous chromosomes to separate) during meiosis, but can also be due to a translocation mutation. For example, Down's syndrome is an example of polysomy where affected individuals possess three copies (trisomy) of chromosome 21.

Polyploidy is a condition in which an organism has three or more sets of chromosomes in each cell. Most organisms have a diploid ($2n$) number of chromosomes in each cell, while polyploids can be triploid ($3n$), tetraploid ($4n$), hexaploid ($6n$) and so on. There are two types of polyploidy: **autopolyploidy** and **allopolyploidy**. Autopolyploidy is known as 'self-polyploidy' and occurs when chromosomes fail to separate during cell division. All the chromosomes are from the same species. Allopolyploidy is known as 'cross-polyploidy' and involves hybridisation between two different species. The resulting hybrid is usually sterile (because homologous chromosomes cannot form pairs during meiosis), but fertility is restored when the chromosome number doubles by a mechanism similar to autopolyploidy.

Mutations occur naturally at a low rate, but this rate can be increased by **mutagens**, such as ionising radiation or certain pesticides. Most mutations are harmful, but a few may increase the fitness of an organism and so spread through the population by natural selection. Mutation is therefore a source of new genetic variation and is essential for evolution.

Environmental change and evolution

Evolution is the process by which new species arise as the result of gradual change in the genetic make-up of existing species over long periods of time. Charles Darwin's theory of evolution by **natural selection** is summarised below.

- All species tend to produce many more offspring than can ever survive. However, the size of populations tends to remain more or less constant, meaning that most of these offspring must die before they reproduce. It also follows that there must be competition for resources such as mates, food and territories. Therefore, there is a 'struggle for existence' between individuals.
- Individuals within a species differ from one another (variation) and many of these differences are inherited (genetic variation).
- Competition for resources, together with variation between individuals, means that certain members of the population are more likely to survive and reproduce than others. These individuals will inherit the characteristics of their parents and evolutionary change will take place through natural selection. Over a long period of time, this process can lead to the considerable differences now observed between living organisms.

Note that a common examination question asks about the evolution of resistance to antibiotics in bacteria. Remember that antibiotics do *not* cause these bacteria to mutate. The mutation (gene for resistance) already exists and the use of antibiotics simply selects those bacteria that carry this mutation. The resistant bacteria then reproduce and over a period of time the whole population becomes resistant.

Natural selection exists in three forms:
- directional selection
- disruptive selection
- stabilising selection

Directional selection is a type of natural selection which occurs when environmental change favours a new form (phenotype) of an organism. For example, in soils contaminated with heavy metals, such as lead, tin, or zinc, natural selection will favour grasses that can tolerate these metals.

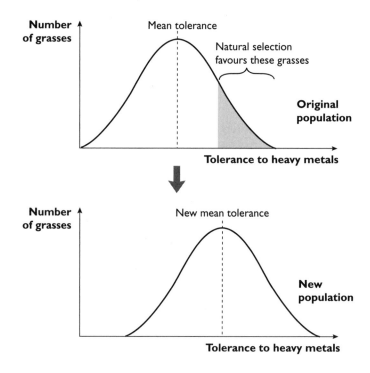

Disruptive selection is a type of natural selection in which the environment favours forms at the extremes of the range of phenotypic variation. The effect of disruptive selection is to eliminate phenotypes in the middle of the range. For example, disruptive selection may have occurred during the evolution of specialised gametes (eggs and sperm). In this case, small gametes (sperm) could be produced in large numbers, and large gametes (eggs) would have sufficient energy to survive and nourish the initial growth of the zygote. Both would have advantages over medium-sized gametes, which would be selected against.

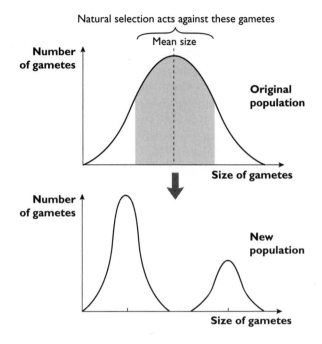

Stabilising selection is a type of natural selection in which the environment acts against forms at the extremes of the range of phenotypic variation. The effect of stabilising selection is to favour phenotypes in the middle of the range. For example, babies whose birth weight is significantly below or above the mean of 3.6 kg have greater mortality than babies of average birth weight.

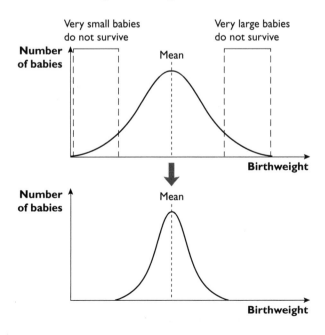

Speciation refers to the formation of new species of organisms.
- **Intraspecific speciation** occurs when a single species gives rise to one or more new species. This requires isolating mechanisms to prevent gene flow between populations of the parent species. Natural selection may then act upon the isolated populations, leading to the development of new species. Individuals may be prevented from reproducing due to a physical barrier preventing interaction, such as a mountain range or river. This **geographical isolation** may lead to **allopatric speciation**. Alternatively, reproduction may be prevented by various other mechanisms, associated with mating, fertilisation and the viability of offspring, known collectively as **reproductive** isolation. This may lead to **sympatric speciation**.
- **Interspecific speciation** occurs when two separate species combine to give rise to a single new species. This involves allopolyploidy (see page 31).

Gene technology

Gene technology refers to the processes involved in changing the characteristics of an organism by inserting foreign genes into its DNA. Gene technology is also known as genetic manipulation or genetic engineering. Some of the techniques used in gene technology are summarised in the flow chart below.

Isolate the gene
- Locate the gene with a *DNA probe* and extract it with **restriction endonucleases**
  or
- Produce the gene from a molecule of **messenger RNA (mRNA)** using reverse transcriptase

↓

Transfer the gene
- Cut open a **plasmid** with a restriction endonucleases, insert the gene and join the pieces of DNA together with DNA ligase
- Insert the recombinant plasmid into a host **micro-organism**, e.g. a **bacterium**
- Check that the bacterium has taken up the plasmid by testing for a marker gene on the plasmid, e.g. resistance to **antibiotics**

↓

Make the product
- Grow the bacteria containing the required gene in a fermenter — they multiply rapidly and produce large quantities of the desired product

---

Gene technology has a wide range of practical applications, from the commercial production of insulin and vaccines, to the creation of transgenic animals and crop plants in agriculture.

The **polymerase chain reaction** (PCR) is a technique used to replicate a particular sequence of DNA. It is used as a means of increasing the quantity of genetic material available for sequencing a particular gene or for measuring gene expression. The basic processes involved in the PCR are summarised in the flow chart below.

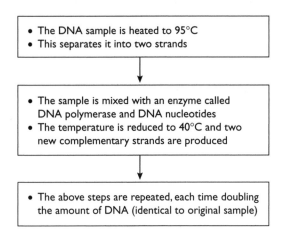

- The DNA sample is heated to 95°C
- This separates it into two strands

- The sample is mixed with an enzyme called DNA polymerase and DNA nucleotides
- The temperature is reduced to 40°C and two new complementary strands are produced

- The above steps are repeated, each time doubling the amount of DNA (identical to original sample)

The PCR can be used to amplify genetic material for use in **genetic fingerprinting**. This is a technique in which an individual's DNA is analysed to reveal a unique pattern of nucleotide sequences. Genetic fingerprinting is used for identification purposes in forensic science, paternity disputes and veterinary science. The techniques used are summarised in the flow chart below.

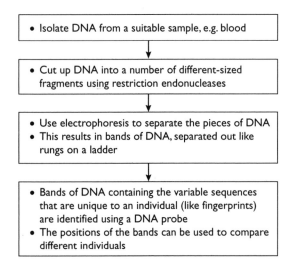

- Isolate DNA from a suitable sample, e.g. blood

- Cut up DNA into a number of different-sized fragments using restriction endonucleases

- Use electrophoresis to separate the pieces of DNA
- This results in bands of DNA, separated out like rungs on a ladder

- Bands of DNA containing the variable sequences that are unique to an individual (like fingerprints) are identified using a DNA probe
- The positions of the bands can be used to compare different individuals

Practical work

You are expected to have carried out practical work to include one breeding experiment to demonstrate the principles of inheritance.

Questions
&
Answers

In this section of the guide there are four mock papers written in the same format as the real unit test papers. All questions are based on the topic areas outlined in the Content Guidance section. When you have completed a paper, ideally under timed conditions — allowing 1 hour 30 minutes each for mock papers 1 and 2 (Unit 5) and 1 hour 10 minutes each for mock papers 3 and 4 (Unit 6) — compare your answers with those of Candidate A and Candidate B. Try to avoid looking at the sample answers and examiner's comments before completing the tests. Make sure that you correct any mistakes and that you study the examiner's comments very carefully. You will get a much better grade if you can avoid the common errors made by candidates in their unit tests.

Examiner's comments

Candidate responses include examiner's comments after each section of the answer. These examiner's comments are preceded by the icon ℮ and indicate where credit is due. In the weaker answers, they also point out areas for improvement, specific problems and common errors, such as poor time management, lack of clarity, weak or non-existent development, irrelevance, misinterpretation of the question and mistaken meanings of terms.

Genetics, evolution and biodiversity (I)

(1) Photosynthesis can be divided into two stages: the light-dependent stage and the light-independent stage.

(a) Where does the light-independent stage take place? (1 mark)

(b) Complete the table below to show the substrates and the products of the two stages of photosynthesis.

	Substrates	Products
Light-dependent stage	Water Inorganic phosphate ADP NADP	ATP ....
Light-independent stage	Reduced NADP ATP	NADP ADP Inorganic phosphate Carbohydrate

(4 marks)

Total: 5 marks

(2) (a) Explain what is meant by the following terms:

(i) *gene* (2 marks)

(ii) *codominant* (2 marks)

The way in which sex is determined in birds is different from that in mammals. In birds, the male has two **X** chromosomes and the female has one **X** and one **Y** chromosome. In one species of bird, the gene for chick colour is sex-linked and carried on the **X** chromosome. The allele for black coloration (**B**) is dominant to that for brown coloration (**b**).

(b) Complete the genetic diagram below to show the cross in which all the male chicks will be black and all the female chicks will be brown.

	Male (**XX**)	Female (**XY**)
Phenotype of parents		
Genotype of parents		
Genotype of chicks		
Phenotype of chicks	Black coloration 50%	Brown coloration 50%

(3 marks)

Total: 7 marks

(3) The size of a population may be affected by both density-dependent and density-independent factors.

(a) Distinguish between the terms *density-dependent* and *density-independent*. (3 marks)

The relationship between two species of mammal, species **X** and species **Y**, was studied in a particular habitat. One of these species was a herbivore and the other was a predator which fed on the herbivorous species. The graph below shows the number of both species over a period of **10 months**.

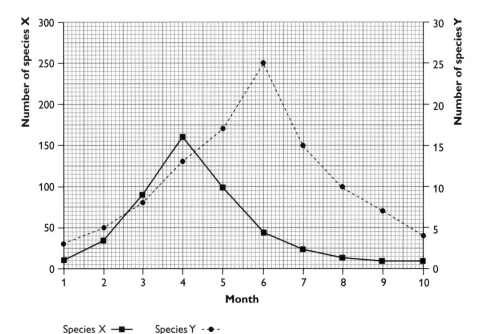

Species X ─■─   Species Y ─◆─

(b) (i) Calculate the rate of increase in the number of individuals of species **Y** between 2 to 6 months. Show your working. (3 marks)

(ii) Identify and explain two reasons why species **Y** was most likely to have been the predator and species **X** the prey. (4 marks)

(iii) Suggest how one abiotic factor might have influenced the results of this investigation. (2 marks)

Total: 12 marks

Synoptic section

(4) *Metabolism* is the sum total of all the biochemical reactions taking place within an organism. Metabolic reactions are controlled by enzymes and can be divided into two groups:

- *anabolism* — synthetic reactions which require energy
- *catabolism* — breakdown reactions which release energy

The various substances involved in metabolism are called *metabolites* and a sequence of biochemical reactions is known as a *metabolic pathway*, as shown in the diagram below.

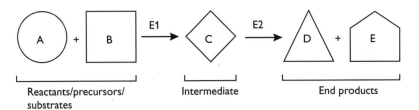

| | Reactants/precursors/
substrates | Intermediate | End products |

Note: E1 and E2 are two different enzymes. This is a very simple metabolic pathway — others may have branches or cycles (e.g. the Krebs cycle).

(a) (i) **State one example of an anabolic reaction and one example of a catabolic reaction in biology.** (2 marks)
(ii) **State two advantages of metabolic pathways.** (2 marks)

The individual reactions that constitute a metabolic pathway are catalysed by specific enzymes, which act according to the lock-and-key hypothesis or the induced fit hypothesis.

(b) Describe what is meant by:
  (i) **the lock-and-key hypothesis** (2 marks)
  (ii) **the induced fit hypothesis** (2 marks)
(c) Identify two factors that will influence the rate of an enzyme-controlled reaction. (2 marks)

Total: 10 marks

(5) Sickle-cell anaemia is caused by a point mutation that changes a single amino acid in haemoglobin. This results in distortion of red blood cells, reducing the amount of oxygen that can be carried. The effect of this mutation is summarised in the diagram below.

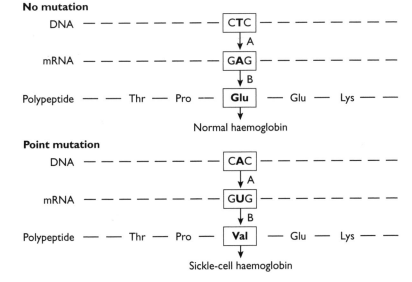

(a) Explain what is meant by the term point mutation. (2 marks)

(b) Name two types of point mutation. (2 marks)

(c) Name processes **A** and **B**, as shown in the diagram. (2 marks)

(d) Suggest why point mutations do not always change the function of the
protein produced. (2 marks)

(e) Explain how a mutation can spread through a population by
natural selection. (4 marks)

Total: 12 marks

(6) Glucose is a monosaccharide which is the main substrate for respiration. The structure of
a molecule of β-glucose is shown in the diagram below.

$$CH_2OH$$

β-glucose

(a) (i) State the molecular formula of glucose. (1 mark)

(ii) Name one polysaccharide that is made of β-glucose. (1 mark)

(iii) Explain how the structure of this polysaccharide is related to the
structure of β-glucose. (4 marks)

The concentration of glucose in the blood is typically 3.4–5.6 millimoles per dm^3. It is
important to maintain this concentration between certain limits and the hormone insulin
plays an important role in this process.

(b) (i) Where in the body is insulin produced? (1 mark)

(ii) What stimulates the release of insulin into the blood? (1 mark)

(iii) Explain how insulin helps to regulate the concentration of glucose
in the blood. (3 marks)

(iv) Name the hormone that has an antagonistic effect to that of insulin. (1 mark)

Total: 12 marks

(7) Discuss the functions of lipids in living organisms. **12 marks**

Genetics, evolution and biodiversity (II)

(1) The table below shows the classification of humans, *Homo sapiens*.

Kingdom	
Phylum	Chordata
	Mammalia
	Primates
	Hominidae
Genus	
Species	

Complete the table by inserting the appropriate word or words in the spaces provided. **5 marks**

(2) (a) Some of the techniques used in gene technology are summarised in the flow chart below.

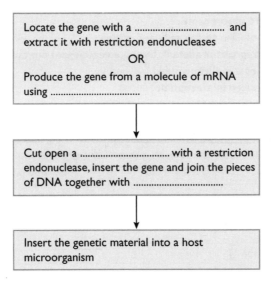

Complete the flow chart by inserting the appropriate word or words in the spaces provided. (4 marks)

(b) Restriction endonucleases occur naturally in bacteria and cut **DNA** between specific base sequences. The diagram below shows three endonucleases and the base sequence positions where they cut **DNA**.

Restriction enzyme	Base sequence

Hpa I

G T T ᵻA A C
C A AᵻT T G
Cut
here

EcoR I

GᵻT T A A C
C A A T TᵻG
Cut
here

Hind III

C G GᵻTA T
G C CᵻAT A
Cut
here

Which of these three endonucleases would be the most useful in
gene technology? Explain your answer. (3 marks)

Total: 7 marks

(3) In rabbits, the allele for black fur, B, is dominant over that for white fur, b. The allele for
long ears, E, is dominant over that for short ears, e. The genes for fur colour and ear
length are on different chromosomes.
(a) Distinguish between the terms *gene* and *allele*. (3 marks)
(b) A rabbit is homozygous for allele B. Giving a reason for your answer in each case, state
how many copies of this allele would be found in:
  (i) a gamete produced by this rabbit
  (ii) a liver cell from this rabbit (4 marks)
(c) (i) Complete the following table to show the results of a genetic cross between a
    rabbit with the genotype BbEe and a rabbit with the genotype bbee.

	First parent	Second parent
Phenotype of parent		
Genotype of parent	BbEe	bbee
Gametes		
Genotypes of offspring		
Phenotypes of offspring		

(4 marks)

(ii) In this cross, what would be the probability of the two rabbits producing an
offspring with white fur and short ears? (1 mark)

Total: 12 marks

Synoptic section

(4) An *adaptation* is any feature of the structure or physiology of an organism that makes it well suited to its environment.

    (a) Describe how a leaf is adapted for efficient photosynthesis.   **(4 marks)**

    (b) Foxes living in Africa have a thinner layer of fur and much larger ears than related species living in cooler climates in Scandinavia. It has been suggested that these foxes may have evolved from a common ancestor in central Europe, which was intermediate in terms of fur thickness and ear size.

        (i) Explain how these features in foxes may represent adaptations to their environments.   **(2 marks)**

        (ii) Suggest how thinner fur and larger ears may have evolved in foxes living in Africa.   **(4 marks)**

                                             Total: 10 marks

(5) Hormones are chemical messengers that are secreted into the blood by endocrine glands. They are transported to target cells, where they bind to specific receptors on the cell surface membrane. The hormone then influences the physiology of the cell in some way.

    (a) Suggest *two* ways in which hormones could influence the physiology of a cell.   **(2 marks)**

    (b) The table below summarises the site of production, target cells and physiological effect of two hormones. Complete the table by inserting the appropriate word or words in the boxes provided.

Hormone	Site of production	Target cells	Physiological effect
ADH			Causes the water potential of blood to increase
	α-cells in the islets of Langerhans in the pancreas	Muscle cells and liver cells	

                                             (4 marks)

    (c) Hormones bind to specific protein receptors on the surface of target cells. Describe how the amino acid sequence of these proteins determines the precise three-dimensional shape of the receptors.   **(4 marks)**

    (d) In non-insulin-dependent diabetes, the pancreas produces enough insulin, but the cells of the body fail to take up glucose in response to the hormone. Suggest two reasons for this observation.   **(2 marks)**

                                           Total 12 marks

(6) (a) (i) Explain what is meant by the term *osmosis*.   **(3 marks)**

      (ii) Name the process by which an organism regulates the water potential of its body fluids.   **(1 mark)**

(b) Water potential in mammals is regulated by the kidneys. The functional unit of the kidney is the nephron and the parts of the nephron that are primarily responsible for the regulation of water potential are the loop of Henle and the collecting ducts.

(i) Describe the roles of the loop of Henle and collecting ducts in the regulation of water potential. (5 marks)

(ii) Suggest why loops of Henle are relatively longer in mammals living in arid (dry) environments than in those living in areas with a plentiful supply of water. (3 marks)

Total: 12 marks

(7) Discuss the importance of surface area-to-volume ratio in biology. **12 marks**

Answers to mock paper 1: Candidate A

(1) (a) In a chloroplast ✗

🖉 This answer is not incorrect, but it is not specific enough to earn a mark. The light-independent stage takes place in the **stroma** of a chloroplast. Remember that questions asking you where certain biological activities take place are fairly common in examinations. Make sure that you know these locations and that you make your answer as specific as possible.

(b)

	Substrates	Products
Light-dependent stage	Water Inorganic phosphate ADP NADP	ATP Reduced NADP ✓ CO_2 ✗
Light-independent stage	Reduced NADP ATP Ribulose bisphosphate ✓ O_2 ✗	NADP ADP Inorganic phosphate Carbohydrate

🖉 Candidate A scores 2 out of 4 marks for part (b). Reduced NADP is correct as a product of the light-dependent stage (there is a clue in the question as this compound is a substrate for the light-independent stage), but the other product should have been **oxygen**. Likewise, the gaseous substrate in the light-independent stage is **carbon dioxide** and not oxygen. Ribulose bisphosphate is correct as another substrate of this stage — this compound acts as an acceptor for CO_2 in photosynthesis. It will help if you remember the simplified word equation for photosynthesis from GCSE biology/science:

$$\text{carbon dioxide} + \text{water} \longrightarrow \text{carbohydrate} + \text{oxygen}$$
$$\text{(substrates)} \qquad\qquad \text{(products)}$$

Overall, Candidate A scores 2 out of 5 marks for this question.

(2) (a) (i) Something that codes for a characteristic ✗.

🖉 No marks for this vague definition. A gene is a section of DNA that codes for the production of a particular polypeptide or protein.

(ii) A condition where both alleles of a gene have an effect ✓.

🖉 This is worth 1 mark. Candidate A understands the idea that both alleles are expressed in the phenotype, but does not make it clear that this is **only in heterozygous organisms**.

(b)

	Male (XX)	Female (XY)
Phenotype of parents	Brown coloration	Black coloration ✓
Genotype of parents	X^bX^b	X^BY ✓
Genotype of chicks	X^BX^b	X^bY ✓
Phenotype of chicks	Black coloration 50%	Brown coloration 50%

Full marks. The trick here is to work backwards from the phenotype of the chicks and to check your answers carefully. The strategy used by this candidate was probably as follows:

- Female chicks must be X^bY as this is the only genotype that would result in brown females.
- The Y chromosome must have been inherited from the female parent (remember that sex determination in birds is the opposite of that found in mammals) and the X^b chromosome must have been inherited from the male parent.
- Only brown females were produced, so the male parent must have been homozygous, i.e. X^bX^b (brown coloration).
- Male offspring were black and so must have inherited X^B from the female parent (as the male parent only has X^b). Therefore, the black male chicks must have the genotype X^BX^b and the female parent must have the genotype X^BY (black coloration).

Overall, Candidate A scores 4 out of 7 marks for this question.

(3) (a) Density-dependent factors are biotic and density-independent factors are abiotic ✗.

No marks. Although it is generally true that density-dependent factors are biotic (and density-independent factors are abiotic), the statement is not specific enough to earn any credit. **Density-dependent factors are factors whose effects are proportional to the density of the population (number of individuals per unit area), such as food supply. Density-independent factors are factors whose effects are independent of the density of the population, such as temperature.**

(b) (i) 20 organisms ✓

Candidate A is correct in that the number of individuals increases from 5 to 25, i.e. an increase of 20 organisms. However, this is only worth 1 mark as the question asks for the *rate* of increase, i.e. the increase in organisms *per month*. The correct answer for 3 marks is **(25−5)/4 = 5 organisms per month**.

(ii) The peak for species Y is later than for species X ✓. This is because extra food (species X, the prey) leads to more of species Y (the predator) surviving and reproducing, so numbers increase ✓.

questions & answers

🖉 A good answer for 2 marks, but the question asks for *two* reasons, so 2 further marks have been lost. Make sure that you read the question carefully! A suitable second reason would be that **the numbers of species Y are lower (about 5 times lower) than those of species X, because one predator feeds on several prey.**

(iii) Temperature ✓ might have affected the survival and/or reproduction of species X, perhaps by affecting the plants on which this species feeds ✓.

🖉 A good answer to part (b)(iii) gives Candidate A 5 out of 12 marks for this question.

(4) (a) (i) Anabolic = protein synthesis ✓; catabolic = respiration ✓
     (ii) Reactions can proceed in a continuous manner, as equilibrium is usually not reached due to products becoming substrates of subsequent reactions ✓. The energy from catabolic reactions can be released in small, controlled quantities ✓.

🖉 Full marks for part (a).

(b) (i) The enzyme is a key and the substrate is a lock ✗.

🖉 This answer is very vague and it is also not correct — the substrate is thought of as a key and the enzyme as a lock. **The lock-and-key hypothesis proposes that the active site of an enzyme has a very specific shape (like a lock) into which the substrate molecule (the key) fits exactly, to form an enzyme–substrate complex.**

(ii) The substrate alters the shape of the active site so that they fit together ✓.

🖉 Candidate A has the right idea, for 1 mark, but does not make it clear that it is the **interaction** between enzyme and substrate that is important, or that only small changes in shape take place. **The induced fit hypothesis proposes that the interaction of an enzyme with its substrate causes the active site of the enzyme to change shape slightly in order to allow the formation of an enzyme–substrate complex. In other words, the substrate induces the enzyme to fit.**

(c) Temperature ✓ and substrate concentration ✓

🖉 Part (c) is correct, for 2 marks. Other possible correct answers include **pH, enzyme concentration** and **the presence of enzyme inhibitors.** Overall, Candidate A scores 7 out of 10 marks for this question.

(5) (a) It is where something is wrong with a person, such as having six fingers ✗.

🖉 This is a vague answer and the example given is quite extreme. A point mutation is **any change in the nucleotide sequence in a gene.** The effects of point mutations are often very minor (sickle-cell anaemia is an exception).

(b) Substitution ✓ and translocation ✗

🖉 Translocation is a type of chromosome mutation and not a point mutation. Other possible answers are: **insertion/addition, deletion** and **duplication.**

(c) A = translation ✗; B = transcription ✗

Candidate A has got these two terms the wrong way around. Try to remember that transCription takes place before transLation (C comes before L in the alphabet). In other words, A = **transcription** and B = **translation**.

(d) The mutation might not cause a change in amino acid in the protein ✓.

This is correct, for 1 mark. A second mark would be awarded for suggesting another reason why point mutations do not always change the function of the protein produced, such as **a different amino acid may not affect the shape of the protein**, or **the shape might change slightly, but this might not affect the function of the protein.**

(e) Some mutations may increase the fitness of an organism ✓ and so spread through the population by natural selection ✓.

This is correct, but only worth 2 out of 4 marks. Remember that you should make at least four separate points to earn 4 marks (often the amount of space given for your answer is a guide). Candidate A should have explained how mutations spread by natural selection, i.e. **competition for resources means that members of the population carrying the advantageous mutation are more likely to survive and reproduce than those without the mutation. The offspring will inherit the mutation from their parents and it will spread through the population.** Overall, Candidate A scores 4 out of 12 marks for this question.

(6) (a) (i) $C_6H_{12}O_6$ ✓
(ii) Starch ✗

Starch is a polysaccharide, but it is composed of long chains of α-glucose, not β-glucose. The correct answer is **cellulose**.

(iii) Starch is actually composed of two different polymers of glucose: amylose (unbranched chains) and amylopectin (branched chains). The chains are usually coiled into a helix, making starch useful as a storage polysaccharide in green plants ✗.

This description of the structure of starch is correct, but the question requires an explanation of how the structure of cellulose is related to the structure of β-glucose. **Cellulose is a polysaccharide composed of long, unbranched chains of glucose molecules. Molecules of β-glucose are arranged in such a way that free hydroxyl (OH) groups stick out from the chain. These can form hydrogen bonds with neighbouring chains. The cellulose chains are arranged in bundles called microfibrils. These microfibrils are cemented together in a matrix of other substances, forming strong but permeable cell walls in plants.**

(b) (i) In the pancreas ✓

This is correct, but the answer could have been more specific. Insulin is produced by β-cells in the islets of Langerhans in the pancreas.

(ii) The brain ✗

🖉 The release of insulin is stimulated by **a relatively high concentration of glucose in the blood**.

(iii) Insulin stimulates the rate of glucose uptake by cells ✓ and activates enzymes that convert glucose to glycogen ✓. Therefore, the concentration of glucose in the blood will fall ✓. This is known as negative feedback.

(iv) Glucagon ✓

🖉 Overall, Candidate A scores 6 out of 12 marks for this question.

(7) A number of important biological molecules are classified as lipids, including triglycerides, which function as energy stores in plants and animals ✓. Phospholipids are important components of cell membranes ✓. Steroids are also classified as lipids and include a number of hormones ✓. Lipids can combine with proteins to form lipoproteins ✓, or with polysaccharides to form lipopolysaccharides ✓, as found in the cell walls of some bacteria ✓.

🖉 This free-prose answer is worth 6 out of 12 marks. It is biologically correct, but very brief. The basic structure of triglycerides and phospholipids could have been described, as could the relationship between their structure and function. Examples of steroid hormones (such as testosterone and oestrogen) would have been useful, as would the transport function of lipoproteins. Finally, other roles of lipids could have been mentioned, such as electrical and thermal insulation, protection from mechanical injury, a source of metabolic water, waterproofing, buoyancy or even scent in insect-pollinated plants!

🖉 **Overall, Candidate A scores 34 out of 70 marks for this paper, which would be a grade D/E.**

Answers to mock paper 1: Candidate B

(1) (a) In the grana of a chloroplast ✗

> 🖉 The grana are the site of the light-dependent stage of photosynthesis. The light-independent stage takes place in the **stroma** of a chloroplast.

(b)

	Substrates	Products
Light-dependent stage	Water Inorganic phosphate ADP NADP	ATP Reduced NADP ✓ O_2 ✓
Light-independent stage	Reduced NADP ATP Ribulose bisphosphate ✓ CO_2 ✓	NADP ADP Inorganic phosphate Carbohydrate

> 🖉 Candidate B scores full marks for part (b) and, overall, scores 4 out of 5 marks for this question.

(2) (a) (i) A section of DNA ✓ that codes for the production of a particular polypeptide or protein ✓.

> 🖉 An excellent definition, for 2 marks.

(ii) Alleles that are both expressed in the phenotype ✓ of a heterozygous organism ✓.

> 🖉 Full marks again. It is definitely worth learning definitions of all key terms — a dictionary of biology might be very useful.

(b)

	Male (XX)	Female (XY)
Phenotype of parents	Black coloration	Brown coloration ✗
Genotype of parents	X^BX^b	X^bY ✗
Genotype of chicks	X^BX^b	X^bY ✓
Phenotype of chicks	Black coloration 50%	Brown coloration 50%

> 🖉 Only 1 mark for part (b). The genotypes of the chicks are correct, but the parental genotypes (and consequently phenotypes) are wrong. These parents would give rise

to a mixture of brown and black males and a mixture of brown and black females. The trick here is to work backwards from the phenotype of the chicks and to check your answers carefully. Overall, Candidate B scores 5 out of 7 marks for this question.

(3) (a) Density-dependent factors are factors whose effects are proportional to the density of the population (number of individuals per unit area) ✓, such as food supply ✓. Density-independent factors are factors whose effects are independent of the density of the population, such as temperature ✓.

📝 Full marks.

(b) (i) Rate of increase = (25−20)/4 = 5 ✓✓

📝 The calculation is correct, but Candidate B has lost a mark for forgetting to put units (organisms per month) in the answer. Remember to **always include units in your answers to calculations**.

(ii) The numbers of species Y are noticeably lower than species X ✓. This suggests that Y is the predator, as energy flow through an ecosystem is not particularly efficient and one predator tends to eat several prey organisms ✓. The population peak for species Y is later than that for species X ✓. This suggests that Y is the predator, because an increase in the number of prey (X) will lead to an increase in the number of predators, because there is more food available, so more predators survive and reproduce ✓.

📝 An excellent answer, for full marks.

(iii) pH ✓

📝 Candidate B scores 1 mark for identifying a suitable abiotic (non-living) factor, but has not suggested *how* this factor might have influenced the results of this investigation, for example by affecting the survival of the plants on which species X feeds. Overall, Candidate B scores 10 out of 12 marks for this question.

(4) (a) (i) Anabolic = photosynthesis ✓; catabolic = glycolysis ✓
(ii) Each step is controlled by a specific enzyme and so there are several points for control in the overall pathway ✓. The steps in the pathway are often spatially arranged in sequence, which makes metabolism much more efficient ✓.

📝 Full marks.

(b) (i) An enzyme's active site has a very specific shape (like a lock) ✓ into which the substrate molecule (the key) fits exactly, forming an enzyme–substrate complex ✓.
(ii) The interaction of the enzyme with the substrate causes the active site of the enzyme to change shape slightly ✓, allowing the formation of an enzyme–substrate complex ✓. Therefore, the substrate induces the enzyme to fit.

Two excellent answers, for full marks.

(c) pH ✓ and enzyme concentration ✓

 Part (c) is correct for 2 marks. Other possible correct answers include **tempera-ture, substrate concentration** and **the presence of enzyme inhibitors**. Overall, Candidate B scores 10 out of 10 marks for this question.

(5) (a) Any change in the nucleotide sequence ✓ in a gene ✓
(b) Insertion ✓ and deletion ✓
(c) A = transcription ✓; B = translation ✓

 Full marks for parts (a), (b) and (c).

(d) The mutation might not cause a change in an amino acid in the protein because some amino acids are coded for by more than one codon ✓. Alternatively, the amino acid might change but it might not affect the shape of the protein ✓.

 An excellent answer, for 2 marks. Another possible answer would be that **the shape might change slightly but this might not affect the function of the protein** (e.g. if the change was in part of an enzyme distant from the active site).

(e) It might be spread by breeding and would kill off most of the population ✗.

 This is not worth any marks. If a mutation is disadvantageous, it is not likely to spread as it will reduce the fitness of the individual carrying it, i.e. they are not likely to reproduce successfully. Candidate B should have explained that **some mutations may increase the fitness of an organism. Competition for resources means that members of the population carrying the advantageous mutation are more likely to survive and reproduce than those without the mutation. The offspring will inherit the mutation from their parents and it will spread through the population.** Overall, Candidate B scores 8 out of 12 marks for this question.

(6) (a) (i) $C_6H_{12}O_6$ ✓
(ii) Cellulose ✓
(iii) Cellulose is a polysaccharide made up of long, unbranched chains of glucose molecules ✓. The molecules of β-glucose are arranged such that free hydroxyl (OH) groups stick out from the chain ✓. These OH groups can form hydrogen bonds with neighbouring chains ✓. The cellulose chains are arranged in bundles called microfibrils to form strong but permeable plant cell walls ✓.

 This is an excellent answer, for full marks.

(b) (i) In the β-cells of the islets of Langerhans in the pancreas ✓
(ii) Not enough glucose in the blood ✗

 The answer to part (ii) is the opposite of what actually happens. Insulin causes the concentration of glucose in the blood to **fall** and its release is **stimulated by a relatively high concentration of glucose in the blood.**

(iii) Insulin stimulates the rate of glucose uptake by cells ✓ and activates enzymes that convert glucose to glycogen ✓. Therefore, the concentration of glucose in the blood will fall ✓. This is known as negative feedback.

(iv) Glycagon ✗

🖉 No mark for part (iv). Candidate B probably knows that the answer is **glucagon**, but has misspelled the word. It is not clear whether 'glucagon' or 'glycogen' was meant and so it has to be marked wrong. **It is important that you try to spell technical terms accurately.** Overall, Candidate B scores 10 out of 12 marks for this question.

(7) Many important biological molecules are classed as lipids. Triglycerides are composed of a glycerol molecule to which three fatty acids are attached by ester bonds ✓. The chemical nature of these molecules makes them ideal as energy stores in plants and animals ✓, because they are compact and contain more energy per gram than carbohydrates ✓. Phospholipids are also lipids and they have a similar structure to triglycerides, except that one of the fatty acids is replaced by a phosphate group ✓. This means that phospholipids have a hydrophilic (water-soluble) phosphate 'head' and a hydrophobic (water-insoluble) fatty acid 'tail' ✓, which is why they are important components of cell membranes ✓.

Steroids are also classified as lipids and include a number of hormones ✓, such as oestrogen and testosterone ✓. Lipids can combine with proteins to form lipo-proteins ✓, which are used to transport lipids in the blood ✓. They can also combine with polysaccharides to form lipopolysaccharides ✓, as found in the cell wall of some bacteria ✓ (MAX). Lipids are important as electrical insulators in the myelin sheath around many neurones and as thermal insulators, forming a layer of subcutaneous fat or blubber below the skin of many animals. They also protect the body from mechanical injury. For example, lipids are packed around the kidneys (which have no skeletal protection) to prevent physical damage. Lipids also play other important roles in plants — as waterproofing on leaves, a buoyancy aid in seeds dispersed by water and as scent in insect-pollinated flowers.

🖉 An excellent free-prose answer which quickly earned maximum marks (MAX) and covered a wide range of appropriate examples in a concise and coherent manner.

🖉 **Overall, Candidate B scores 59 out of 70 marks for this paper, which would definitely be a grade A.**

mock paper

Answers to mock paper 2: Candidate A

(1)

Kingdom	Animals ✓
Phylum	Chordata
Class ✓	Mammalia
Family ✗	Primates
Order ✗	Hominidae
Genus	Homo
Species	sapiens ✓

This answer is worth 3 out of 5 marks. 'Animals' is correct in the first space, although **Animalia** would be a better answer. Candidate A has correctly named the missing taxonomic groups, but has mixed up order and family. Make sure that you remember the right order for these groupings. Finally, note that you need both *Homo* and *sapiens* in the final two spaces to earn a single mark, because *Homo sapiens* is given in the stem of the question!

(2) (a)

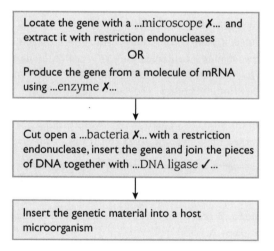

Candidate A scores just 1 out of 4 marks for part (a). It is not possible to locate individual genes with a microscope! The correct answer for the first space is **gene probe**. The answer 'enzyme' in the second space is not incorrect, but it is not specific enough to earn a mark. The enzyme that converts mRNA to DNA (the gene) is **reverse transcriptase**. In the third space it is a **plasmid** that is cut open with a restriction endonuclease.

(b) EcoR I ✓, because it produces 'sticky ends' ✓.

⌨ This response is worth 2 out of 3 marks. Candidate A has not extended the answer to explain *why* sticky ends are useful — they provide an area of overlap between the vector and the foreign gene which makes gene insertion more effective. Overall, Candidate A scores 3 out of 7 marks for this question.

(3) (a) An allele is a section of DNA that codes for the production of a particular polypeptide or protein. A gene is one of the different forms of an allele ✗.

⌨ No marks for this answer. Candidate A has made the (fairly common) mistake of mixing up these two terms. Remember that **a gene is a section of DNA that codes for the production of a particular polypeptide or protein,** whereas **an allele is one of the different forms of a gene.** Examples can sometimes be useful in questions such as these, for example **a gene controls a character, such as eye colour, and alleles control different forms of this character, such as blue, green or brown eyes.**

(b) (i) 23 copies, one on each chromosome of this haploid cell ✗.
(ii) 46 copies, one on each chromosome of this diploid cell ✗.

⌨ Candidate A has recognised correctly that gametes are haploid and that liver cells (somatic cells) are diploid. However, there are two significant mistakes here, so no marks are scored. The first mistake is not to realise that body cells contain **two** alleles for each gene, located at a specific locus on a single pair of homologous chromosomes. Gametes have one of each of a homologous pair of chromosomes (following meiosis) and therefore contain **one** allele. The second (common) mistake is to think that rabbits have 46 chromosomes just because humans do! Each species has a characteristic number of chromosomes (e.g. pea plants have 14), so do not assume that there are always 46 chromosomes present.

(c) (i)

	First parent	Second parent
Phenotype of parent	Black fur/long ears	White fur/short ears ✓
Genotype of parent	BbEe	bbee
Gametes	BE bE Be be	be ✓
Genotypes of offspring	BbEe bbEe	Bbee bbee ✓
Phenotypes of offspring	1 black fur/long ears; 1 white fur/long ears; 1 black fur/short ears; 1 white fur/short ears ✓	

⌨ An accurate, clear answer for 4 marks. Remember the advice about doing genetic crosses, given on page 29.

(ii) 1:1:1:1 ✗

⌨ This answer is a genetic ratio, *not* a probability. We would expect 1 in 4 rabbits to have white fur and short ears, so the probability is $\frac{1}{4}$ or 0.25 (25%). Overall, Candidate A scores 4 out of 12 marks for this question.

Synoptic section

(4) (a) It has a large surface area ✓.

📝 This is correct, but not worth 4 marks! Try to think of four separate marking points, i.e. four features of leaves that make them adapted for efficient photosynthesis. These might include: **large surface area** (for maximum light absorption), **thin lamina** (for efficient gas exchange), **network of veins** (for the transport of photosynthetic pigments to the rest of the plant) and **many palisade cells** (which contain large numbers of chloroplasts for efficient photosynthesis).

(b) (i) Thinner fur means that foxes in Africa can lose heat more efficiently in the hot climate ✓.

📝 This is worth 1 out of 2 marks. Candidate A has not mentioned the big ears, whose large surface area would enable the foxes to lose excess heat.

(ii) Foxes with thinner fur and larger ears are more likely to survive in Africa ✓. So they breed and eventually all foxes will have thinner fur and larger ears ✓.

📝 This answer is worth 2 out of 4 marks. It is partially correct, but lacks the detail required for 4 marks. A more detailed answer would include most of the points listed below.

- **The original fox population that colonised Africa showed variation in terms of fur thickness and ear size.**
- **Some of this variation was genetic in nature.**
- **Foxes with thinner fur and larger ears had more efficient thermoregulation and so were more likely to survive and reproduce than foxes with thicker fur and smaller ears.**
- **Genes for thinner fur and larger ears were more likely to be passed on to subsequent generations (compared with genes for thicker fur and smaller ears). Eventually, the whole population had thinner fur and larger ears than their ancestors.**

Note that this type of answer would be valid as an explanation of any evolved adaptation. Overall, Candidate A scores 4 out of 10 marks for this question.

(5) (a) Changing the permeability of the cell surface membrane ✓ or activating an enzyme inside the cell ✓.

(b)

Hormone	Site of production	Target cells	Physiological effect
ADH	Kidney ✗	Nephron ✗	Causes the water potential of blood to increase
Glucagon ✓	α-cells in the islets of Langerhans in the pancreas	Muscle cells and liver cells	Causes an increase in the concentration of blood glucose ✓

🖉 Candidate A scores 2 out of 4 marks for part (b). ADH acts on the kidney, but it is produced in the **pituitary gland**. The answer 'nephron' in the second space is not incorrect, but is not specific enough to earn the mark. ADH acts on the cells of the **distal convoluted tubules** and **collecting ducts** of the nephron.

(c) The amino acid sequence is the primary structure of the protein ✓. The primary structure determines the precise three-dimensional shape of the receptors.

🖉 Again, this is not incorrect, but not detailed enough for 4 marks. The primary structure of a protein determines its **secondary structure, which is the regular coiling or folding of the polypeptide chain** (e.g. into an α-helix or β-sheet). The primary and secondary structures then determine the **tertiary structure, which is the irregular folding of the polypeptide chain — the specific shape of which is held together by various bonds, including hydrogen bonds, ionic bonds and disulphide bonds.**

(d) Insulin is not released in response to an increase in the concentration of glucose in the blood ✓. Alternatively, the insulin might bind to its target cells, but fail to trigger a physiological response, i.e. no increase in cell membrane permeability to glucose ✓.

🖉 A very good answer to part (d) gives Candidate A 7 out of 12 marks for this question.

(6) (a) (i) The movement of water ✓ from a more concentrated solution to a less concentrated solution.

🖉 This answer is worth 1 out of 3 marks. The reference to 'more concentrated' and 'less concentrated' is too vague — we don't know if Candidate A is talking about the concentration of the **solvent** (water) or the **solute**. You should always describe osmosis in terms of water potential to avoid this problem. Furthermore, Candidate A has not made it clear that osmosis takes place across a selectively permeable membrane. A better answer, therefore, would be that **osmosis is the diffusion of water from a region of high (less negative) water potential to a region of low (more negative) water potential across a selectively permeable membrane.**

(ii) Homeostasis ✗

🖉 Once again, this answer is correct, but too vague to earn the mark. The correct term is **osmoregulation**.

(b) (i) The loop of Henle consists of a thin descending limb, which is permeable to water, and a thick ascending limb, which is impermeable to water ✓. Movement of ions across the walls of the loop of Henle allows it to act as a countercurrent multiplier ✓, building up the sodium concentration in the medulla of the kidney ✓.

🖉 This answer is partially correct, for 3 out of 5 marks. It does not explain how the high concentration of sodium ions in the medulla helps to regulate water potential, nor does it mention the role of the collecting ducts. **The high concentration of**

sodium in the medulla causes water to move out of the collecting ducts by osmosis, resulting in the production of concentrated urine. The volume of water reabsorbed into the blood depends on the permeability of the cells lining the collecting duct, which is regulated by ADH.

(ii) Because mammals living in arid environments need to conserve water ✓.

This gains just 1 mark. The answer does not explain how longer loops of Henle help these mammals to conserve water, i.e. that **longer loops of Henle cause a greater concentration of sodium in the medulla and so more water is reabsorbed into the blood and less is lost in urine.** Overall, Candidate A scores 5 out of 12 marks for this question.

(7) Surface area-to-volume (SA/V) ratio is the ratio between the surface area of an organism and its volume ✓. In general, the larger the size of an organism, the smaller is the SA/V ratio ✓. Therefore, larger organisms need specially adapted structures to exchange material with the environment ✓. For example, the ileum is adapted for the absorption of the products of digestion by being very long and highly folded, increasing its SA/V ratio ✓. This surface area is further increased by the presence of many villi ✓. The lungs are another example of a specialised exchange surface as they contain millions of alveoli to increase the SA/V ratio for gas exchange ✓.

This is a reasonable (if brief) account of the importance of SA/V ratio, for 6 out of 12 marks. Candidate A could have explained *why* larger organisms have a smaller SA/V ratio and *why* very small organisms do not need specialised exchange systems. The examples could have been elaborated a little more (e.g. the presence of microvilli on the surface of villi to further increase SA/V ratio) and a wider range of examples could have been used. For example: changes in body shape to increase SA/V ratio, as seen in flatworms; the importance of surface area in biological reactions, as seen in the action of digestive enzymes (e.g. lipase acting on lipids in the presence and absence of bile); and the importance of SA/V ratio in thermo-regulation, such as in the example of foxes' ears in different climates in question 4 of this paper.

Overall, Candidate A scores 32 out of 70 marks for this paper, which would be a grade D/E.

Answers to mock paper 2: Candidate B

(1)

Kingdom	Animalia ✓
Phylum	Chordata
Class ✓	Mammalia
Order ✓	Primates
Family ✓	Hominidae
Genus	Homo
Species	sapiens ✓

[e] Full marks.

(2) (a)

> Locate the gene with a ...gene probe ✓... and extract it with restriction endonucleases
>
> OR
>
> Produce the gene from a molecule of mRNA using ...RNA-dependent DNA polymerase ✓...

↓

> Cut open a ...plasmid ✓... with a restriction endonuclease, insert the gene and join the pieces of DNA together with ...DNA polymerase ✗...

↓

> Insert the genetic material into a host microorganism

[e] Candidate B scores 3 out of 4 marks here. The enzyme that converts mRNA to DNA (the gene) is commonly known as **reverse transcriptase**, but RNA-dependent DNA polymerase is also correct. In the final space, it is **DNA ligase** that joins the pieces of DNA together to make recombinant DNA.

(b) Hpa I ✗, because it produces straight ends that the gene can stick to ✗.

[e] This is not correct; in fact it is almost the opposite of the correct answer. The most useful endonuclease is **EcoR I, because it produces 'sticky ends'. Sticky ends provide an area of overlap between the vector and the foreign gene, which makes gene insertion more effective.** Overall, Candidate B scores 3 out of 7 marks for this question.

(3) (a) A gene is a section of DNA that codes for the production of a particular polypeptide or protein ✓. An allele is one of the different forms of a gene ✓.

Therefore, a gene controls a character, such as eye colour, and alleles control different forms of this character, such as blue or brown eyes ✓.

(b) (i) One copy ✓, as gametes are haploid cells and so only contain one of each pair of homologous chromosomes and each chromosome carries one copy of the allele B ✓.

(ii) Two copies ✓, as liver cells are diploid cells and so contain pairs of homologous chromosomes, with each chromosome carrying a copy of the allele B ✓.

🖉 Full marks for parts (a) and (b).

(c) (i)

	First parent	Second parent
Phenotype of parent	Black fur, long ears	White fur, short ears ✓
Genotype of parent	BbEe	bbee
Gametes	Bb Ee	bb ee ✗
Genotypes of offspring	Bbee bbEe ✗	
Phenotypes of offspring	1 black fur, short ears; 1 white fur, long ears ✗	

🖉 Only 1 mark is awarded for part (c)(i). Only one of each pair of alleles is found in a gamete, i.e. gametes from the first parent could be **BE**, **Be**, **bE** or **be** (*not* Bb and Ee), and those from the second parent could only be **be** (*not* bb and ee). From this point on, it is inevitable that the genotypes and phenotypes of the offspring will be wrong (see Candidate A's response for the correct answer). Remember the advice about doing genetic crosses given on page 29.

(ii) Zero ✗

🖉 This answer is correct for the cross described in (c)(i), but since Candidate B got that part wrong, this must also be wrong! We would expect 1 in 4 rabbits to have white fur and short ears, so the probability is $\frac{1}{4}$ or 0.25 (25%). (See Candidate A's response.) Overall, Candidate B scores 8 out of 12 marks on this question.

Synoptic section

(4) (a) It has a large surface area and a transparent cuticle for maximum light absorption by the photosynthetic tissue ✓. The leaf blade (lamina) is thin to allow efficient gas exchange with the environment ✓. The leaf contains a network of veins to provide water from the roots and to transport the products of photosynthesis to the rest of the plant ✓. The leaf is packed with palisade cells close to its upper surface and these cells contain large numbers of chloroplasts for efficient photosynthesis ✓.

🖉 This is an excellent answer, for full marks.

(b) (i) African foxes have adaptations to lose heat in the hot climate. A thinner layer of fur means that more heat can be lost through the skin ✓. Larger ears have a bigger surface area-to-volume ratio, so heat is lost from the blood as it flows through the ears ✓.

(ii) The original fox population that colonised Africa would have shown variation in terms of fur thickness and ear size ✓. Some of this variation was genetic in nature and therefore subject to natural selection ✓. Foxes with thinner fur and larger ears had more efficient thermoregulation and so were more likely to survive and reproduce than foxes with thicker fur and smaller ears ✓. Genes for thinner fur and larger ears were therefore more likely to be passed on to subsequent generations than genes for thicker fur and smaller ears ✓. Eventually, the whole population of foxes would have thinner fur and larger ears than their ancestors.

🖉 A very good, detailed answer for part (b). Overall, Candidate B scores 10 out of 10 marks for this question.

(5) (a) Activating a gene ✓ or inhibiting an enzyme inside the cell ✓.

(b)

Hormone	Site of production	Target cells	Physiological effect
ADH	Pituitary gland ✓	Collecting ducts in nephrons ✓	Causes the water potential of blood to increase
Insulin ✗	α-cells in the islets of Langerhans in the pancreas	Muscle cells and liver cells	Causes a decrease in the concentration of blood glucose ✗

🖉 Candidate B scores 2 out of 4 marks for part (b). The hormone produced by the α-cells in the islets of Langerhans is **glucagon** and this hormone causes an **increase in the concentration of blood glucose**, i.e. it is antagonistic to insulin.

(c) The sequence of amino acids in a protein is known as the primary structure of the protein ✓. The primary structure determines the secondary structure, which is the regular coiling or folding of the polypeptide chain into an α-helix or β-sheet ✓. The primary and secondary structures determine the tertiary structure, which is the irregular folding of the polypeptide chain ✓. The precise three-dimensional shape of the receptors is held together by various bonds (e.g. hydrogen, ionic and disulphide) ✓.

🖉 This is an excellent answer, for full marks.

(d) There might be no insulin receptors (or a smaller number of receptors) on the surface of target cells ✓ or perhaps the number of receptors does not change but their affinity for insulin is lower (perhaps due to a change in shape of the protein) ✓.

A very good answer to part (d) gives Candidate B 10 out of 12 marks for this question.

(6) (a) (i) The diffusion of water ✓ from an area of high (less negative) water potential to an area of low (more negative) water potential ✓ through a semi-permeable membrane.

This response is worth 2 out of 3 marks. Candidate B has made the mistake of using the inaccurate term 'semi-permeable' instead of **selectively permeable**.

(ii) Osmoregulation ✓

(b) (i) The loop of Henle consists of a thin descending limb (permeable to water) and a thick ascending limb (impermeable to water) ✓. Movement of ions across the walls of the loop of Henle enables it to act as a countercurrent multiplier ✓, building up the concentration of sodium in the medulla of the kidney ✓. The high concentration of sodium ions in the medulla of the kidney causes water to move out of the collecting ducts by osmosis, leading to the production of concentrated (hypertonic) urine ✓. The amount of water reabsorbed into the blood depends on the permeability of the cells lining the collecting duct, which is regulated by antidiuretic hormone (ADH) ✓.

A very good answer, for full marks.

(ii) Longer loops of Henle cause a greater concentration of sodium ions to accumulate in the medulla ✓ and so more water is reabsorbed into the blood and less is lost as urine ✓. This helps mammals living in arid environments to conserve water ✓.

Full marks for part (e)(ii). Overall, Candidate B scores **11 out of 12** marks for this question.

(7) Surface area-to-volume (SA/V) ratio is the ratio between an organism's surface area and its volume ✓. As an object increases in size, its SA/V ratio decreases ✓. Therefore, in general, the larger an organism, the smaller is its SA/V ratio ✓. A small, one-celled organism, such as *Amoeba*, has a very large SA/V ratio and it is therefore able to exchange materials with its environment by diffusion through its body surface ✓. Larger organisms, however, need specially adapted structures to exchange material with the environment ✓, unless they alter their body shape (only suitable for relatively small organisms), as do flatworms ✓. One example of specialisation is the ileum, which is adapted for the absorption of the products of digestion by being very long and highly folded, increasing its SA/V ratio ✓. This surface area is further increased by the presence of many villi ✓, and cells lining the surface of the villi have their surface area increased by the presence of microvilli ✓. The lungs are another example of a specialised exchange surface as they contain millions of alveoli to increase the SA/V ratio for gas exchange ✓. SA/V ratio can also be important in thermoregulation — a high ratio will enable effective heat loss in hot climates, as seen in the large ears of African foxes and the tall stature of African people compared with those living in the Arctic ✓. Finally,

SA/V ratio is important in biological reactions. For example, the enzyme lipase breaks down lipids much faster if their surface area has been increased by the action of bile in the small intestine ✓.

☑ Full marks for an excellent free-prose answer — concise and detailed, with a range of examples.

☑ **Overall, Candidate B scores 59 out of 70 marks for this paper, which would definitely be a grade A.**

Synoptic paper (I)

(1) (a) Unicellular microorganisms have been found living in deep trenches in the Pacific
Ocean. These microorganisms contain DNA that is composed of a double helix of
nucleotides, but which contains six different nucleic acid bases, identified as **K, L, M, P,
Q** and **R**. Of these, **P, Q** and **R** were found to be pyrimidine bases.
   (i) What type of bases are **K, L** and **M**? (1 mark)
   (ii) Identify one base that could not pair with **P**. (1 mark)
   (b) Studies of the **DNA** from these microorganisms revealed the sequence of bases in
one particular gene that coded for a peptide composed of a total of seven amino acids.
The sequence is shown below, with the bases coding for the C-terminal amino acid on
the left.

K-K-L-P-L-P-M-R-Q-P-L-P-P-L-P-R-Q-Q-R-Q-Q

When the peptide for which this gene codes was hydrolysed, it yielded amino acids in
the proportions shown in the table below.

Amino acid	Number of amino acids per peptide
A	1
B	3
C	2
D	1 (at C-terminal end)

Using this information, answer the following questions about the genetic code in this
microorganism.
   (i) How many bases are present in a codon specifying a single amino acid?
      Explain your answer. (2 marks)
   (ii) Work out the actual sequence of amino acids in the peptide and write them
      in the correct sequence in the boxes provided (the C-terminal is on the left).

(4 marks)
Total: 8 marks

(2) The graph below shows the effects of light intensity, carbon dioxide concentration and
temperature on the rate of photosynthesis of a crop plant.

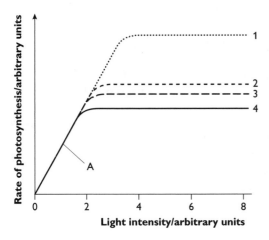

	CO$_2$ concentration/%	Temp/°C
1	0.06	30
2	0.06	20
3	0.03	30
4	0.03	20

(a) Explain which factor is most likely to be limiting the rate of photosynthesis at point **A**. (2 marks)

(b) The growth of crops in glasshouses in winter is limited by the rate of photosynthesis. A glasshouse has a light intensity of 4 arbitrary units, a temperature of 20°C and a carbon dioxide concentration of 0.03%. Which one of the following conditions, **X, Y** or **Z**, would result in the greatest increase in growth of the crop plant? Explain your answer.

X — increasing the carbon dioxide concentration from 0.03% to 0.06%
Y — increasing the temperature from 20°C to 30°C
Z — increasing the light intensity from 4 to 8 arbitrary units (2 marks)

(c) Suggest why it is not advisable to increase the temperature in a glasshouse on a dull winter day. (2 marks)

(d) The rate of photosynthesis can also be limited by water availability. The graph below shows changes in the mean diameter of xylem vessels in three different species of plant, measured on a hot dry day in August.

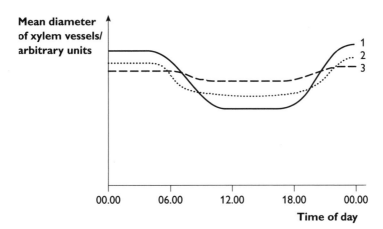

(i) Explain the changes observed in the mean diameter of xylem vessels in plant 1. (4 marks)

(ii) Which of the plants 1, 2 or 3 is likely to be best adapted to a dry environment? Explain your answer. (2 marks)

(iii) Describe one feature you would expect in the leaves of a plant adapted to a dry environment and explain how this feature helps the plant to survive. (3 marks)

Total: 15 marks

(3) Write an essay on nervous coordination in mammals. **15 marks**

Synoptic paper (II)

(1) The table below shows the results of an investigation into how the distribution of roots of three species of tree varied with depth. The figures are given as percentages of the total root dry mass of the species concerned.

Soil depth/m	Species A	Species B	Species C
0–1	72.9	65.9	63.6
1–2	16.2	27.7	15.7
2–3	7.5	5.8	12.9
3–4	2.7	0.6	5.6
4–5	0.7	0	1.7
5–6	0	0	0.5
Total dry mass/ kg per tree	13	29	57

(a) Calculate the dry mass of root tissue found in soil between 1–2 m in species A. Show your working.   (2 marks)

(b) Describe the relationship between the percentage of root tissue and soil depth in species B.   (2 marks)

(c) All three of these species grow in hot, dry conditions. Which species would you expect to grow best if the ground was lightly sprinkled with water at regular intervals? Explain your answer.   (2 marks)

(d) Suggest why species C is able to survive better than the other two species during lengthy periods of hot, dry weather.   (2 marks)

Total: 8 marks

(2) The Lincoln index (mark–release–recapture method) can be used to estimate the number of individual animals in a population:

$$\text{estimated population size} = \frac{S_1 \times S_2}{R}$$

where:
- S_1 = number of organisms captured and marked
- S_2 = number of organisms captured in second sample
- R = number of organisms recaptured

(a) State three assumptions that must be made when using this technique.   (3 marks)

(b) In estimating the size of a population of Colorado beetles, 84 beetles were trapped, marked and released. A week later, a second sample was captured. Of these, 33 were marked and 15 were not.

Calculate the estimated size of the Colorado beetle population. Show your working.   (3 marks)

(c) Colorado beetles are important pests of potatoes. The graphs below show the results of an experiment using a chemical pesticide and biological control (a predator) on two plots of potatoes infested with beetles.

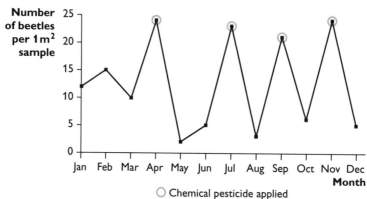

○ Chemical pesticide applied

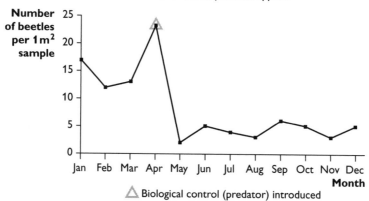

△ Biological control (predator) introduced

(i) Suggest an explanation for the changes in the beetle population before the use of chemical or biological controls. (2 marks)

(ii) Describe and explain the effect of introducing predators on the beetle population. (3 marks)

(iii) Using evidence from the graphs, state two possible advantages of biological control over chemical control. (2 marks)

(iv) State two possible disadvantages of biological control. (2 marks)

Total: 15 marks

(3) Write an essay on the roles of water in the lives of organisms. 15 marks

Answers to mock paper 3: Candidate A

(1) (a) (i) Nucleotide bases ✗

🖉 This is correct, but not specific enough to earn a mark. K, L and M are **purine** bases. Remember that the bases in DNA are either purines or pyrimidines.

(ii) R ✓

🖉 This is correct (Q would be the other base that could not pair with P) — two pyrimidine bases cannot form a complementary pair.

(b) (i) Seven, because there are seven amino acids ✗.

🖉 Candidate A appears to have misread the question. There are 7 codons (coding for 7 amino acids) represented by 21 bases. Therefore, there are 21/7 = 3 bases in each codon.

(ii)

| D | B | A | B | B | C | C |

🖉 This is correct, for 4 marks. You are told that amino acid **D** is at the C-terminal end, so this amino acid must come first in the sequence. Then you should notice that the codon P-L-P occurs three times, so must code for amino acid **B** in the second, fourth and fifth boxes. This reasoning also applies to codon M-R-Q, which occurs once and therefore codes for amino acid **A** in the third space. Finally, codon R-Q-Q occurs twice at the end of the chain, so amino acid **C** must go in the sixth and seventh boxes. Overall, Candidate A scores 5 out of 8 marks for this question.

(2) (a) Light intensity ✓ because it is low at point A.

🖉 This answer is worth 1 out of 2 marks. The word 'low' in the answer is meaningless — what is 'low'? We know light intensity is limiting at point A because **if we increase the intensity of the light, the rate of photosynthesis increases.**

(b) Y, because increasing the temperature increases the rate of photosynthesis ✗.

🖉 It is true that increasing the temperature increases the rate of photosynthesis, but increasing the carbon dioxide concentration from 0.03% to 0.06% has a greater effect, i.e. it results in the greatest increase in growth. Therefore, the correct answer is X.

(c) Because the extra heat will be lost to the environment ✗.

🖉 On a dull winter day it will probably be **light intensity** that is limiting the rate of photosynthesis, so **increasing the temperature will have no effect.** Furthermore, there will be costs associated with increasing the temperature and this money would be wasted.

(d) (i) The rate of transpiration is greatest in the middle of the day ✓ and so water is being pulled up the xylem vessels at a greater rate ✓. This means that the diameter of the xylem vessels is reduced.

📝 This answer is worth 2 out of 4 marks. Candidate A could have said *why* the rate of transpiration is greatest in the middle of the day (between 12.00 and 18.00 hours), i.e. **because the temperature is at its highest**. The reason for the reduction in the mean diameter of the xylem vessels should be explained. **The water molecules in the xylem vessels are held together by cohesion (forces of attraction between the molecules) and the column of water is under tension because transpiration is pulling the water upwards and gravity is pulling it downwards. A higher rate of transpiration means that the tension is greater and so the mean diameter of xylem vessels is reduced.**

(ii) Plant 1, because it responds the most to changes in environmental conditions ✗.

📝 **Plant 3** is best adapted to a dry environment **because its rate of transpiration is hardly affected by the increased temperatures during the day, i.e. it is adapted to these environmental conditions.**

(iii) The plant might have leaves that are reduced to spines ✓ to minimise the surface area ✓ and so reduce the rate of transpiration (conserving water) ✓.

📝 A good answer to part (b)(iii) gives Candidate A a total of 6 out of 15 marks for this question.

(3) The nervous system is made up of neurones, which are cells specialised for the conduction of nerve impulses. Neurones are well adapted for conducting impulses (caused by movement of sodium ions), having an elongated shape and specialised structures to form connections with receptors, effectors and other neurones using sinapses.

Many neurones are coated with myeline (produced by Schwann cells), which helps to speed up the conduction of nerve impulses. Nerve impulses are caused by the movement of sodium ions in and out of neurones and jump across gaps using neurotransmitters.

The central nervous system is the brain and spinal chord. The brain is the organ that controls bodily functions by coordinating the activities of the nervous system. In the brain is the hyperthalamus (which controls homeostasis) and the medulla, which regulates heart rate.

📝 Synoptic essays are marked using three criteria. **Scientific content** (up to 13 marks) refers to the quality of biology in the essay. In this case, there is some factually correct and relevant material, but it is slightly below average overall and so scores 5 out of 13 marks. **Balance** (up to 2 marks) refers to the coverage of the essay and whether the material is relevant. In this case, several of the main areas are mentioned briefly and there is no irrelevant material, but there is very little about the nerve impulse. It therefore scores 1 out of 2 marks. **Coherence** (up to 2 marks) refers to the quality of scientific communication in the essay. In this case, the writing is reasonable, but there is no real introduction or conclusion and there are some spelling mistakes (e.g. 'sinapses', 'myeline', 'chord' and 'hyperthalamus'). Therefore, this essay scores 1 out of 2 marks for coherence. Overall, the essay scores 5+1+1 = 7 out of 15 marks. (See Candidate B's answer for a good example of this essay.)

Overall, Candidate A scores 18 out of 38 marks for this paper, which would be a grade D/E.

mock paper

Answers to mock paper 3: Candidate B

(1) (a) (i) Purine bases ✓

    (ii) Q ✓

ℓ Both correct. In part (ii) R would be the other base that could not pair with P — two pyrimidine bases cannot form a complementary pair.

(b) (i) 3 bases in each codon ✓

ℓ This is correct but only earns 1 out of 2 marks because no working has been shown. In this case, 21 bases code for 7 amino acids so there are 21/7 = 3 bases in each codon.

    (ii)

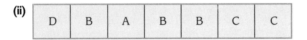

D	B	A	B	B	C	C

ℓ This is correct, for 4 marks. For an explanation of this exercise in logic, see Candidate A's answer. Overall, Candidate B scores 7 out of 8 marks for this question.

(2) (a) Light intensity ✓

ℓ This answer is worth 1 out of 2 marks. Light intensity is the limiting factor at point A, but Candidate B has not explained *why*. We know light intensity is limiting at this point because **if we increase the intensity of the light, the rate of photosynthesis increases**.

(b) X ✓, because increasing the light intensity will have no effect (it is not limiting) and increasing the carbon dioxide concentration has a greater effect on the rate of photosynthesis than increasing the temperature ✓.

(c) On a dull winter day, light intensity will probably be limiting the rate of photosynthesis, so increasing the temperature will have no effect ✓. Heating the greenhouse will therefore be a waste of energy and money ✓.

(d) (i) Plants transpire at night. Therefore, during the day (when the plant doesn't need to transpire) the xylem vessels are constricted to prevent water going to the leaves.

ℓ This answer is not worth any marks. **The rate of transpiration is greatest in the middle of the day (between 12.00 and 18.00 hours) because the temperature is at its highest. Therefore, water will be being pulled up the xylem vessels at a greater rate. This means that the diameter of the xylem vessels will be reduced. This is because the water molecules in the xylem vessels are held together by cohesion (forces of attraction between the molecules) and the column of water is under tension because transpiration is pulling the water** upwards and gravity is pulling it downwards. **A higher rate of transpiration means that the tension is greater and so the mean diameter of xylem vessels is reduced.**

(ii) Plant 3 ✓, because its rate of transpiration is hardly affected by the increase in temperature during the day. In other words, it is adapted to such environmental conditions ✓.

(iii) The plant might have rolled leaves with sunken stomata ✓ and a thick cuticle ✓ in order to reduce the rate of transpiration, thereby conserving water ✓.

A good answer to parts (b)(ii) and (iii) gives Candidate B a total of 10 out of 15 marks for this question.

(3) Nervous coordination is needed in large multicellular organisms, such as mammals, in order to make sure that the activity of physiological systems within the body is controlled according to the needs of the individual. A nervous system is also needed to ensure that the mammal can respond to external stimuli, such as light or sound, and respond appropriately. This essay will address the organisation of the nervous system in mammals, the nature of the nerve impulse and the role of receptors and effectors in coordination.

Neurones are cells specialised for the conduction of nerve impulses. They are well adapted for conducting impulses, having an elongated shape and specialised structures that form connections with receptors, effectors and other neurones via synapses. There are three basic types of neurone. Sensory neurones transmit impulses from a receptor to the central nervous system. Motor neurones transmit impulses from the central nervous system to an effector, and intermediate neurones connect sensory and motor neurones within the central nervous system.

Many neurones are coated with myelin, which is a mixture of phospholipid and cholesterol. Myelin is produced by Schwann cells and is laid down as insulating blocks along the length of the neurone. Points at which there is no myelin sheath are known as nodes of Ranvier. Myelin speeds up the conduction of an impulse, as it allows the impulse to jump from one node to the next. This is known as saltatory conduction.

A nerve impulse is a signal that travels along a neurone. Information is transmitted through the nervous system by impulses. The neurone at rest has a potential difference of −70 mV across its cell surface membrane. In other words, the inside is negative relative to the outside because there is a high concentration of sodium ions outside the cell. Following stimulation, the neurone becomes depolarised as sodium ions enter the cell via ion channels (making it positive relative to the outside). During repolarisation, potassium ions leave the cell, restoring the negative potential difference. A sodium-potassium pump then restores the resting potential by actively transporting potassium into the cell and sodium out of the cell.

Impulses are transmitted between neurones via a synapse. When a nerve impulse arrives at a synapse, vesicles containing neurotransmitter (such as acetylcholine) fuse with the presynaptic membrane and release their contents into the synaptic cleft. The neurotransmitter then diffuses across the cleft and attaches to receptor molecules on the postsynaptic membrane. This causes ion channels to open and sodium ions enter the postsynaptic neurone, leading to an action potential (impulse) in this neurone.

The nervous system is divided into the central and autonomic nervous systems. The central nervous system consists of the brain and spinal cord and is responsible for coordinating the activities of the nervous system. The brain is specialised to perform certain functions, for example the cerebrum controls voluntary behaviour, learning and memory and the medulla oblongata coordinates breathing and heart rate. The spinal cord is the part of the central nervous system that is enclosed by the backbone. It consists of a central cavity containing cerebrospinal fluid, surrounded by a core of grey matter (non-myelinated neurones) and an outer layer of white matter (myelinated neurones). The white matter contains numerous longitudinal neurones, which conduct impulses to and from the brain. The spinal cord also plays an important part in coordinating many reflexes. The autonomic nervous system is the part of the nervous system that is responsible for controlling the involuntary activities of the body. It is divided into two sections. The sympathetic nervous system is responsible for preparing the body for action, for example increasing heart rate, and the parasympathetic nervous system is responsible for relaxing the body, for example decreasing heart rate.

In conclusion, receptors transmit information via nerve impulses to the central nervous system which, together with the autonomic nervous system, coordinates the activities of the body. This system allows mammals to coordinate their internal activities and to respond appropriately to the environment, thus increasing survival chances and permitting this group of animals to occupy a wide range of environmental niches.

☑ Synoptic essays are marked using three criteria. **Scientific content** (up to 13 marks) refers to the quality of biology in the essay. In this case there is a great deal of factually correct and relevant material and it is an excellent essay — it scores 13 out of 13 marks. **Balance** (up to 2 marks) refers to the coverage of the essay and whether all the material is relevant. In this case, all of the main areas are covered in good detail and there is no irrelevant material. It therefore scores 2 out of 2 marks for balance. **Coherence** (up to 2 marks) refers to the quality of scientific communication in the essay. In this case, the writing is very good, there is an introduction and a conclusion and no spelling mistakes. Therefore, this essay scores 2 out of 2 marks for coherence. Overall, the essay scores 13+2+2 = 17 marks, but can only be awarded the maximum of 15 out of 15 marks.

☑ **Overall, Candidate B scores 32 out of 38 marks for this paper, which would be a grade A.**

Answers to mock paper 4: Candidate A

(1) (a) $(13/16.2) \times 100 = 80.2\%$ ✗

💬 Candidate A has used the correct figures, but has calculated a percentage instead of a mass. The correct answer is $(16.2/100) \times 13 = 2.106\,kg$.

(b) As the soil gets deeper, there are fewer roots ✓.

💬 Candidate A has correctly identified the general pattern in the data, but has only made one point (for 1 mark). Alternative answers are that there is no root tissue below 4 m, or the figures in the table could have been used to calculate that 93.6% of root tissue is found between 0–2 m.

(c) C, because it has the biggest mass of roots ✗.

💬 Although a large mass of roots will be an advantage in getting water from the soil, remember that the whole tree will be very large and so this extra water may not result in more growth. To take advantage of water close to the surface (before it evaporates), it would be advantageous to have a larger proportion of root tissue close to the surface. Therefore, the correct answer is A.

(d) Because it has the greatest mass of roots ✓.

💬 This answer is worth 1 out of 2 marks. Candidate A could have pointed out that the roots penetrate deeper into the ground in species C (up to 6 m), enabling the tree to access water at these depths, where there is no competition from the other two species of tree. Overall, Candidate A scored 2 out of 8 marks for this question.

(2) (a) That the marked beetles mix randomly with the rest of the population ✓.

💬 This is correct, but Candidate A has only given one assumption and therefore can only get 1 mark. The other assumptions are that: **marking does not affect the probability of survival of the beetles; marking persists throughout the investigation; there is no movement of beetles into or out of the population (i.e. no immigration or emigration); and that there are no births or deaths during the investigation.**

(b) Estimated total population size $= (84 \times 48)/33 = 122$ beetles ✓✓✓.

(c) (i) An abiotic factor such as temperature ✓ could have affected the survival of the beetles by affecting their metabolic rate ✓.

💬 Two acceptable suggestions, for 2 marks.

(ii) The number of beetles is reduced ✓ and stays relatively constant at this new lower level ✓.

This answer is worth 2 out of 3 marks. It is a reasonable *description* of the data, but no attempt has been made to *explain* the observations, i.e. that **numbers are reduced due to beetles being eaten by predators**, or that **the population stays relatively constant due to previous environmental resistance (density-dependent) factors being insignificant (due to the low number of beetles)**, or that **predator–prey relationships explain the slight fluctuations in population size.**

(iii) The average number of beetles is lower with biological control ✓.

This is correct, but it is only *one* advantage. The other advantage (from the graphs) is that **there is no need to reapply the predator** (as there is for the chemical control).

(iv) The predator may become a pest in its own right ✓, and biological control is relatively slow when compared with pesticide ✓.

Both marks are gained here. Candidate A could also have said that **the pests are never completely eliminated and so there is always some damage to crops.** Overall, Candidate A scores 11 out of 15 marks for this question.

(3) Water is used as a solvent in living organisms and as a reactant in metobolic reactions. For example, water is used in photosinthesis and in hydrolysis reactions in breaking down big molecules.

Water is used in sweting to cool the body down and in tears when we cry. Some plants and animals, such as fish, live in water so it is a very important liquid.

We have to drink lots of water to keep healthy — humans don't usually drink enough. We would die very quickly without water, so it is the most important thing in the world.

Synoptic essays are marked using three criteria. **Scientific content** (up to 13 marks) refers to the quality of biology in the essay. In this case, there is some factually correct and relevant material, but it is very minimal and so scores 3 out of 13 marks. **Balance** (up to 2 marks) refers to the coverage of the essay and whether all the material is relevant. In this case, very few of the main areas are mentioned and the last two sentences are not particularly relevant. It therefore scores 0 out of 2 marks for balance. **Coherence** (up to 2 marks) refers to the quality of scientific communication in the essay. In this case, the writing is reasonable (if very brief), but there is no introduction or conclusion and there are some spelling mistakes (e.g. 'metobolic', 'photosinthesis' and 'sweting'). Therefore, this essay scores 1 out of 2 marks for coherence. Overall, the essay scores 3+0+1 = 4 out of 15 marks. (See Candidate B's answer for a good example of this essay.)

Overall, **Candidate A scores 17 out of 38 marks for this paper, which would be a grade D/E.**

Answers to mock paper 4: Candidate B

(1) (a) $(7.5/100) \times 13 = 0.975 \, \text{kg}$ ✗

    ☝ Candidate B has used the correct method, but has taken the wrong figure from the table (7.5% instead of the correct figure of 16.2%). Be very careful when extracting figures from tables or graphs.

(b) There are fewer roots as the soil gets deeper ✓ and no root tissue below 4 m ✓.

    ☝ Two points for 2 marks.

(c) A ✓, because it has the biggest proportion of its roots close to the surface (in the first metre) and so will be able to absorb a lot of the water before it evaporates ✓.

    ☝ Full marks.

(d) Because it has the greatest mass of roots ✓ and the roots penetrate deeper into the soil (up to 6 m) ✓ (MAX). This enables species C to obtain water at these depths, where there is no competition from species A and B.

    ☝ More than enough for 2 marks. Overall, Candidate B scores 6 out of 8 marks for this question.

(2) (a) Marking does not affect the probability of survival of the beetles ✓. There is no immigration or emigration of beetles into or out of the population ✓. There are no births or deaths of beetles during the investigation ✓.

    ☝ Full marks. Candidate B could also have said that **the marked beetles mix randomly with the rest of the population** or that **marking persists throughout the investigation.**

(b) Estimated total population size $= (84 \times 33)/48 = 58$ beetles ✓.

    ☝ Only 1 mark awarded here. Remember that the Lincoln index states that: estimated total population size $= S_1 \times S_2/R$ where S_1 is the number of organisms caught and marked, S_2 is the number of organisms captured in the second sample and R is the number of marked organisms recaptured, i.e. $(84 \times 48)/33 = 122$ beetles. Candidate B scores 1 mark for S_1 (84 beetles), but loses the other 2 marks for mixing up S_2 and R.

(c) (i) A biotic factor such as food availability ✓ could have affected the survival of the beetles, as the population would grow when food was plentiful and fall when food was scarce ✓.

    (ii) The number of beetles is reduced ✓ because the beetles are eaten by predators ✓. The numbers then show slight fluctuations due to predator–prey relationships ✓.

(iii) The average number of beetles is lower with biological control ✓ and there is no need to reapply biological control (as there is for chemical control) ✓.

(iv) The pests are never completely eliminated and so there is always some crop damage ✓ . Biological control is slow compared with chemical control ✓.

📝 Full marks for part (c). Candidate B could also have said that **the predator may become a pest in its own right.** Overall, Candidate B scores 13 out of 15 marks for this question.

(3) Water is an important inorganic chemical found in all living organisms. It performs a wide variety of roles: as a solvent, a transport medium, a substrate in biochemical reactions and a habitat for many plants and animals. This essay will attempt to describe and explain the large number of functions of water in living organisms.

The chemical formula of water is H_2O. It is a dipolar molecule because the hydrogen atoms have a slightly positive charge and the oxygen atoms have a slightly negative charge. This means that water molecules can form hydrogen bonds and it explains the unique physical properties of water. For example, it has a high latent heat of vaporisation and it is therefore an effective coolant. Mammals use this feature when sweating during thermoregulation. Water also has a high specific heat capacity and it is therefore an ideal habitat for many living organisms.

Water is an important solvent in living organisms and it therefore has a key role as a transport medium. In animals it is a vital constituent of blood and tissue fluid, transporting substances such as monosaccharides, amino acids, vitamins (e.g. vitamin C) and minerals, such as iron. It transports red and white blood cells around the body of most animals. Water is also the main transport medium in plants, moving the products of photosynthesis from the leaves to the rest of the plant. It transports mineral ions from the roots via the xylem, where the adhesive and cohesive properties of water help to move these substances over great distances, especially in trees.

Water is an important constituent of cells, playing a role in biochemical reactions such as the hydrolysis of macromolecules, for instance proteins and polysaccharides. It is also a substrate in photosynthesis, supplying hydrogen ions during the light-dependent stage for the reduction of NADP (which is consequently used to reduce CO_2 to carbohydrates during the light-independent stage).

Water is incompressible and so acts as a form of support. This can be seen in herbaceous plants, where turgidity of tissues helps to keep the plants upright, and in hydrostatic skeletons, such as that found in earthworms. Water also acts as a lubricant in mammalian skeletons, particularly within synovial joints.

In conclusion, water performs a wide variety of important roles in all living organisms.

Synoptic essays are marked using three criteria. **Scientific content** (up to 13 marks) refers to the quality of biology in the essay. In this case, there is a great deal of factually correct and relevant material and it is an excellent essay, scoring 13 out of 13 marks. **Balance** (up to 2 marks) refers to the coverage of the essay and whether all the material is relevant. In this case, all of the main areas are covered in good detail and there is no irrelevant material. It therefore scores 2 out of 2 marks for balance. **Coherence** (up to 2 marks) refers to the quality of scientific communication in the essay. In this case, the writing is very good, there is an introduction and a conclusion and no spelling mistakes. Therefore, this essay scores 2 out of 2 marks for coherence. Overall, the essay scores 13+2+2 = 17 marks, but can only be awarded the maximum of 15 out of 15 marks.

Overall, Candidate B scores 34 out of 38 marks for this paper, which would be a grade A.